Cam Zimak

CLOSE TO
THE
HEART

For Emily
and Benjamin

CLOSE TO THE HEART

Compiled by Paul and Mary Knowles

ENGLISH GARDEN PUBLISHERS
NEW HAMBURG, ONTARIO

ISBN 0-9698873-1-0

Patrons:
Hanson Pontiac-Buick-GMC, New Hamburg, Ontario;
Harold Schmidt, Baden, Ontario;
Riverside Brass and Aluminum Foundry, New Hamburg, Ontario;
Erb Transport Ltd., New Hamburg, Ontario;
Fusion Consulting, Komoka, Ontario;
Schlueter Chev-Olds, Waterloo, Ontario;
Josslin Insurance Brokers Ltd., New Hamburg, Ontario;
Friesens, Book Division, Altona, Manitoba;
Doris and Harry Traplin, Kitchener, Ontario;
Rose and Ralph Knowles, RR1 Eden, Ontario;
M&M Meat Shops, Kitchener, Ontario;
Expressway Motors Ltd., New Hamburg, Ontario;
Gary and Mary Houslander, Waterloo;
Mersynergy Charitable Foundation, St. Jacobs, Ontario;

Cover design by:
Dave Sapelak Design, New Hamburg, Ontario.

Text design and typesetting by:
English Garden Publishers, New Hamburg, Ontario.

Printed by:
Friesens, Book Division, One Printer's Way, Altona, Manitoba R0G 0B0.

Publisher:
English Garden Publishers,
61 Seyler Street, New Hamburg, Ontario, Canada N0B 2G0
(519) 662-2287

CONTENTS

ACKNOWLEDGEMENTS

This book would not be possible without the amazing generosity of two groups of people: the authors who have made their unpublished works available, at no cost, to further the fight against breast cancer; and the business people and other individuals who have contributed funds to assist with the production of the book.

The financial contributors have enabled us to completely cover the cost of publishing *"Close to the Heart"*, so that all profits from this book will go directly to the organizations doing research into prevention and cure for breast cancer.

Thanks to the patrons of this project, whose donations make it possible: Hanson Pontiac-Buick-GMC of New Hamburg, Ontario; Harold Schmidt of Baden, Ontario; Riverside Brass and Aluminum Foundry of New Hamburg, Ontario; Erb Transport Ltd. of New Hamburg, Ontario; Fusion Consulting of Komoka, Ontario; Schlueter Chev-Olds of Waterloo, Ontario; Josslin Insurance Brokers Ltd. of New Hamburg, Ontario; Friesens, Book Division, Altona, Manitoba; M&M Meat Shops of Kitchener, Ontario; Expressway Motors Ltd. of New Hamburg, Ontario; Gary and Mary Houslander of Waterloo; Mersynergy Charitable Foundation of St. Jacobs, Ontario; and our parents, Doris and Harry Traplin of Kitchener, and Rose and Ralph Knowles of RR1 Eden, Ontario.

The authors and poets have made our lives in the past year a real joy, as wonderful works of art have arrived in the mail or on our fax machine, week by week. We are very grateful that these writers — most of whom knew nothing of Mary and Paul Knowles — have been willing to offer the product of their art and soul to this project.

We must note that these contributions have underscored the importance of our cause. We gave no direction to our writers, asking only for unpublished short stories, poems, or creative non-fiction. We did, of course, tell them the purpose of the book.

In response, nearly half the stories and poems submitted deal with cancer, most often breast cancer. There could be no greater testament to the importance and impact of this terrible disease.

We're pleased to present this book, not only as a means to a healthy end, but also as a means of presenting some very fine, never-before-published stories and poems to our readers.

FOREWORD

by Mary Knowles

I am a breast cancer survivor. I am one of legions of women who are grateful for each day, each month, and each medical follow-up appointment that demonstrate that we remain free of any signs of the spread of this terrifying disease.

Since being diagnosed in September of 1992 my life has changed immeasurably. The changes didn't happen overnight, however. First you get through the immediate, physical stuff ... surgery, more surgery, radiation treatments, extreme pain, debilitating tiredness, soreness, tenderness, and finally just discomfort. You move through the stages like a sleepwalker, following instructions and trying not to think about the fact that what you have is CANCER! That word, and what it signifies, is too big and too scary to fit into your consciousness.

Time passes; the treatments are over for now. Slowly, the frightening, sinking feeling takes hold: "I have (or should I say 'I have had'?) cancer. Am I going to die?"

One evening, while resting in bed the day after my lumpectomy, I drifted into a light sleep. I awoke with a wonderful feeling that it had all been a bad dream. I was so relieved, so happy. Then I lifted my hand to my chest and felt the heavy bandages, along with a searing flash of pain. I can barely describe the horrible stab of fear and dread I experienced as I realized that it was NOT a dream ... I had cancer. Later, when my husband came to bed, I told him what had happened.

We both cried.

Friends and relatives have been extremely supportive and helpful during this difficult time. A local support group was formed by two fellow breast cancer survivors; it helps to know that you are not alone with your fear and your anger. Both of those women have experienced a spread of cancer to bones and liver; one of them died in October of 1995.

One in nine women in Canada will experience the fear, the pain, the uncertainty ... the terror of breast cancer. Of every three women diagnosed, one will die.

I don't want these kind of statistics clouding my daughter's life; in fact, her odds of contracting breast cancer are four times those of someone with no family history of the disease. I recently read that daughters and sisters of breast cancer victims or survivors have a 50% chance of contracting the disease in their lifetime!

Something has to change. We need to find out why there is more incidence of breast cancer in the United States and Canada, particularly near the Great Lakes regions, than anywhere else in the world. We need to know why the mortality rate for this disease has not changed in over 40 years, despite our many advancements in medicine in general. We need to understand the links between diet, lifestyle and this disease. We need to ask why many women have to wait up to four months to begin radiation treatments after diagnosis. We also need answers and action in many other areas.

Greater public awareness of this disease is one goal in publishing this book. From a greater awareness should come an increased demand for action. Action in the form of research, support for those with breast cancer, support for their families, new and less invasive procedures and treatment, and so much more.

The idea for this book came from a heartfelt desire to raise money for the prevention of breast cancer. I want to thank all the Canadian writers and poets who agreed to give us their unpublished works for inclusion in this book. I hope you enjoy their many examples of fine and sensitive writing. A special thank-you to our friend, David Sapelak, for his intuitively beautiful cover design. And to my husband, whose idea this book was, this message: I couldn't and wouldn't want to have faced these past few years without your love, courage and sense of humour.

Many months after my treatment was finished, my daughter, then 13 years old, showed me a poem she had written about the experience of having her mother diagnosed with breast cancer. She regularly writes poetry as a way of venting her feelings, both happy and sad; angry and frustrated. Here's her poem:

JUST A LITTLE

by a survivor's daughter

A mother and daughter walk down the street,
With smiles across their faces.
The mother is a 36 year old woman,
On her way to the office.
She's telling her daughter about her garden,
And how her roses are growing much better
Since she transplanted them.
She knows her daughter could bike down the street
In two minutes.
It's taking ten minutes to walk.

A daughter and mother walk down the street,
With smiles across their faces.
The daughter is a 13 year old "young woman",
On her way to school.
She's reminding her mother that she has to
Pick her up at 4:45 after her school play rehearsal,
So they can go shopping.
She knows her mother could drive to work
In two minutes.
It's taking ten minutes to walk.

The mother had gotten cancer this year
So she was slowing down a little,
Not rushing like before.
The daughter thought she would lose her mother this year,
So she is spending more time with her mother,
Not taking her for granted, like before.

Each of them realizes that life is more
Precious than they once thought.
Sure, life will go on, but they'll treat
Each other just a little better.
Because who knows what's around the corner?

To all of you who have purchased this book, for yourself or as a gift for someone special, thank you. May our daughters, and their daughters, face a future free of the threat of breast cancer.

Carol Shields

Carol Shields is the author of *The Stone Diaries*, for which she won the Pulitzer Prize in 1995. She has also written *The Republic of Love*, *The Orange Fish*, *Swann*, *Various Miracles*, and *Happenstance*. She lives in Winnipeg, Manitoba.

STOP!

The Queen has dropped out of sight. And at the busiest time of the court season too, what with the Admiral's Ball coming up, and the People's Picnic. No one knows where she's disappeared to. Has she gone to the seaside? Unthinkable. A person who is sensitive to salt water, to sand, to beach grass and striped canvas does not traipse off to the seaside. Well, where then? It used to be that she would spend a few days in the mountains in late summer. She loved the coolness, she said, the grandeur. But now her sinuses react to balsam and pine. And to the inclines of greenness and shadow.

No, she is a stay-at-home queen. A dull queen. Not exactly beloved, but a queen who is nevertheless missed when she is absent. People are starting to talk, to wonder. They understand that the pollen count is high, and so it is not unreasonable that she remain enclosed in her tower. But why have the windows been bricked in? Can it be that she has developed an intolerance to sunlight too? Poor soul, and just at the turning of the year with the air so fine and pale.

Music, of course, has been anathema for years. Bugles, trumpets and drums were confiscated in the first triannulus of her reign, and stringed instruments — violins, cellos — inevitably followed. It was heartbreaking to see, especially the moment when the Queen's own harp was smashed by hammers and the pieces buried deep in the palace garden.

Simple nourishment has always been for her a form of torture. Fruits and vegetables, meal and milk bring on duodenal spasms, but, worse, she is unable to bear the shape of a spoon in her mouth. The finest clothing rubs and chafes. The perfume of flowers causes her to faint, and even oxygen catches in her windpipe so that she coughs and chokes and calls for the court physician.

Ah, the physician! What grave responsibility that man bears. It was he, after all, who first recognized the danger of ragweed and banished it from the realm. Then roses. Then common grass and creeping vines. It was he who declared the Queen to be allergic to her courtiers, to her own children, to the King himself.

But at least life went forward. Acts of proclamation. The Admiral's Ball, already mentioned. And the Spring Rites on the royal parade grounds where the Queen could be glimpsed by one and all, waving her handkerchief, bravely blessing her subjects with the emblem of her disability. People are fed by that kind of example. Yes, they are. People find courage in stubborn endurance.

But recently the Queen has dropped out of sight, and matters have suddenly worsened. There has been an official announcement that clocks and calendars are to be destroyed. It is forbidden now to utter the names of the days and months, to speak of yesterday or tomorrow or next week. Naturally there will be no Spring Rites this year, for the progression of seasons has been declared unlawful. Meteorologists have been dismissed from their positions and weather disallowed. The cause of Her Majesty's affliction has been identified. It has been verified absolutely. It seems the measured substance that pushes the world this way and that, the invented sequenciality that hovers between the simple raising and lowering of a tea cup, can no longer be tolerated by the Queen.

At last the people understand why the palace windows have been closed up. The temporal movement of the sun and stars must be blocked from her view. Rhythmic pulsations of light threaten her existence, suggesting as they do the unstoppable equation that attaches to mass and energy. She lives in the dark now, blindfolded, in fact. Her ears, too, have been covered over for fear she will hear the cries of birds, a cock at dawn, a swallow, or an owl hooting its signature on the night sky. She no longer speaks or thinks, since the positioning of noun and verb, of premise and conclusion, demands a progression that invites that toxic essence, that mystery.

But they have overlooked her heart, her poor beating queenly heart. Like a mindless machine it continues to add and subtract. A whimsical toy, it beeps and sighs, singing and songing along the jointed channels of her blood. Counting, counting. Now diminishing.

Now swelling. Insisting on its literal dance. Tick-tock, tick-tick. Filling up with deadly arithmetic.

Rosemary Sullivan

Rosemary Sullivan is a poet whose books include *The Garden Master, The Space a Name Makes, By Heart: Elizabeth Smart / A Life*, and *Blue Panic*. She has won the Gerald Lampert Award, League of Canadian Poets. She lives in Toronto.

MARKET DAY

The smell of a green world breaks through the dust
I stand on a rim of suction
colours pull me in:
crimson pomegranates and cool yellow grenadillos
green lucma, pale white toronja, pumpkin and quince
They ring bells against my eyes
Women in hooped skirts and black stovepipe hats
children in bright rebozos staring from their backs
A ragged girl, peacock bright, offers me a pineapple:
"Oje gringa—mucho dinero," she smiles slyly
Four bluebirds flutter in her net
She would have me take them to my country
The mangoes and melons and papayas call out in sweetness
fruits of water in a dry world
above the market, mud houses gleam in tiers

ARISTOPHANES' HERMAPHRODITE

People are sentimental
They love a love story
Imagine an egg —
four arms, four legs, two heads
twisting like periscopes on a tubular neck
the globular man/woman sitting plaintively
at the backs of our imaginations
He said it was sliced like an apple
for pickling and now the pieces
go skulking for each other in the dark
But love is an old story we all edit
Imagine the fights
in the great domestic egg
Would one side or back
(but which is back or front?)
be stronger? When it wanted to go
forward (but what is forward?)
would it hoist the other legs on its back
and tramp off on its own private journeys?
Is that why men dream
of hoisting women in the air
and walking into sunsets?
It's an old dream.
Would the front half do all the talking
while the back loomed like a shadow
always excluded from conversations
the half one took for granted

and no one remembered
peeking over a shoulder to slip a word in?
Would they search each other's bodies like braille
four hands groping in the night?
Asleep in the terrible obscurity of their intimacy
would they dream the utopian dream
of separation?
Love is an old joke
people keeping missing
It's harder than that
to keep the seal intact
meet the other front-on—
face to lonely face

AFTERNOON WITH MY FATHER

That day sharing the rain on St. Antoine Street
For me just rain. You walked back sixty years
to a child's face pressed to a window
waiting for a day to clear

The place still stands, an old memory
squeezed between new flats, stern
its frowning roof as grey as you
On the stairs, stains of your feet
mounting years to the second floor

The funeral parlor once owned
by a sweetheart's father—they moved
to money—scowls down the freeway
At the corner the variety store sells buttermilk
a bike leans against its window
like a painting of your vintage—
boy delivering the beer

In the back lane we search out the wall
where you played <u>Relevio!</u>
In the camera frame I find you
leaning back to hide   UCK YOU. We laugh
You can only obscure one letter.

You talk of Harry and Jim
home from the lumber camp, nursing a beer,

their shout of "Cops"; the wall too high—
<u>Caught!</u>— the cell with the hookers and the pimps
A child's afraid.

The church with the foreign priest
where you went when your sins were big
your game to sit in the mass
tracing the woodwork riding the heads of the saints
the route to the sky where St. Antony stood
with his birds — home free

The Irish champ! You gave your title up
knowing you could kill.
Dancing the nights at Smalls.
A woman on a blind date. Fate. Five kids.
A job for fifty years.

Today you wear the Irish tweed,
the bracelet we bought, not yet engraved
with our names. The special shoes
to cushion your feet from doctors cadging a fee.

Your life had many walls
you learned to call home base
On the street where you are a child
I walk. We play <u>Relevio</u>. Caught,
you tag me free.

Maggie Siggins

Maggie Siggins is the author of *Bassett: A Biography, Brian and the
Boys: A Story of Gang Rape, A Canadian Tragedy: JoAnn and Colin
Thatcher,* and *Revenge of the Land,* which won the Governor-
General's Award for Non-Fiction in 1992.
She lives in Regina, Saskatchewan.

REBECCA, 1883

She looked like a frightened hen, her pointed nose white with anxiety, her neck taut, her thin arms fluttering. *Do be careful! I shall die if you drop it.* Never mind that the crate had already traveled two thousand miles across the country. She flapped some more as her husband and his brother carefully lifted the heavy wooden box out of the wagon. Only when it was finally deposited in that miserable space Dougald liked to call a parlour did she relax a little.

She had driven them all to distraction with her worrying. *What if the snow comes, locks us in like prisoners? It could sit at the station for months — probably they would be careless, leave it outside — and then what condition would it be in?* Even though Rebecca had yet to endure her first prairie winter, she understood already, and with a burrowing desperation, that the contents of that wooden box represented her only link to a serenity that had once formed the temple of her daily life.

For a month she had mulled over where to put it — *This wall perhaps, no that corner where the sun's hot rays won't touch it.* As Dougald and Colin lifted it into position, she noticed with satisfaction the magnificent gloss of the rosewood, as rich and lustrous as burgundy satin. Yet once it was set down, she knew that it was totally out of place and always would be.

An extravagance of gilt curlicue flourishes, the commode stood on ridiculous brass feet with tufts of hair playing about the stout angles, plump toes and whittled nails. Not even England's royal lion would possess such outlandish and monstrous paws, Dougald had mocked. It was an outrage in so plain and sad a room. Though Rebecca knew this at once, she said not a word to her husband.

He had railed against the idea of shipping something so heavy, so frivolous as this ridiculous piece of furniture; the cost would be an extravagance, the inconvenience absurd. With all the toughness she could muster, Rebecca had fought back. *It was my grandmother's precious treasure, given to her beloved daughter because she knew she would never see her again. And my mother refused to leave England without it just as I will not budge unless it comes with me. I will not.*

In reality, Dougald was a mild-manned man devoted to his difficult but seductive wife and so the beast with the fat bronze paws came to dominate the miserable little hut squatting in the vast, forbidding prairies.

Winter soon struck. The winds screamed in rage, the snow crushing in its wake. Crouched in the corner of the bed, her shawl pulled up over her head, Rebecca imagined that their feeble little hut was caught in the maw of a terrible creature who, out of spite, was intent on shaking his victims to death. And she didn't feel much better when the storm finally howled itself out. Watching the heavy snow pile up past the window ledge, she felt sure they would all suffocate. She was terrified when Dougald finally had to go out to feed the livestock. *Supposin' you don't find your way back, how am I to care for the children? How will we escape this terrible place?*

But the barn wasn't far, and Dougald, as usual, had taken precautions. A bucket of manure, still steaming, had been placed just inside the back door of the shack — Rebecca had been disgusted but too frightened to protest — and now as he stamped in the direction of the barn, he threw shovelfulls of the stuff along his route. Perfect signposts, he called out. Rebecca's only response was a scowl.

She wouldn't allow four-year-old Eddie or two-year-old Stella to use the outhouse. Nor did she have enough nerve herself to venture into the smothering white, even for something so private. Dougald solved the problem with large feedbuckets. Chamberpots fit for the Queen Mother herself wouldn't you say, he had quipped, desperate to relieve the gloom. Rebecca huddled closer to the stove.

The stink became such that the waste had to be tossed out the front door. The children hooted with laughter as the urine, a hideous bright yellow, etched exotic patterns in the snow. Eddie screeched, There is an elephant out there, I'm sure of it, but his mother soured the bright moment: *No such creature could live in this dreadful place.*

That night the temperature dropped to 35 degrees below zero. Rebecca was so cold that she cried herself to sleep. The next day she wrote her father, he who had insisted life with Dougald would be so safe: I woke up this morning and my eyelids were frozen solid together. What she didn't mention was that in screaming out her terror, she had disgraced herself. Dougald was embarrassed, ashamed, and lectured at her: You've upset yourself and the children needlessly.

Freezing as it was, the Carmichaels assiduously kept to the part of the bed each had laid claim to. On rare occasions Dougald would lay his hand on his wife's slender hip; Rebecca, awake instantly, would jerk away. It was her resentment, growing more poisonous every day that turned her against him, but *the very idea of giving birth in this godforsaken place petrifies me. I am, after all, not an animal.* Dougald's advances soon ceased. Any zest for life he might have had, and he was seldom a passionate man, had froze in his bones, not so much from the cold — he didn't really mind that — but by the bitterness which endlessly played on Rebecca's face.

Even the long-awaited arrival of spring brought little relief. Rebecca had been sitting on the stoop, basking for a few moments in the still wan sun, when she first smelled it. She knew what it was immediately. Once, on her father's farm, her younger brother had fallen from the barn roof and impaled himself on the prongs of a pitchfork. It had been Rebecca's job to dress his wound, and while at first it had seemed to heal, eventually gangrene had set in. She remembered gagging at the smell, and it was this horrible stench that was now playing about on the spring breezes. Dougald's explanation didn't help much: the railway workers had allowed their horses to graze on the open prairie, not realizing how savage the winters would be; the animals had frozen to death; the local population of coyotes and buzzards was not large enough to do the job; the carcasses were not stripped clean and the flesh putrefied in the warming sun. *Macabre, brutal for a place that in the morning light can be so beautiful.*

Dougald had always planned that the family would live in town for the summer, but given his wife's state of mind, he thought they had better make the move quickly. And he was eager, too — there was money being made and he wanted in on it.

His journey out west had taken years of careful saving, careful planning. The sacrifices required had been much more difficult for Rebecca than himself because he didn't care about anything but grabbing a stake in "the glorious granary of the British Empire", as the government pamphlet had so nicely put it. As skilled a carpenter as found anywhere, he had worked day and night at any job that came along, saving every little cent, until finally he had accumulated a nice nest egg. Invested in the building boom exploding just then in Moose Jaw, the dollars would surely mushroom before his eyes.

The idea of running a hotel appealed to Rebecca far more than farming out on the lonely prairie. All winter long she had pondered over the name and finally came up with The Enterprise House. That surely set just the right tone — not a fancy place but clean, with tasty food and fresh sheets and towels. Since she was good at it, she wouldn't mind the cooking, although she was shocked that *beefsteak as tough as old hide* — she had to pound it for a good ten minutes before she could throw it in the stew pot — cost forty cents a pound. *Those ugly wrinkled apples cost ten cents each and you can hardly make a decent pie out of them.* Still, she went at her job with zest.

With only the occasional help of his brother, who was working for the railroad, Dougald had constructed the two-storey wooden structure, all sharp angles and irregular planes, on the lot he had bought on Main Street between McCork Lumber and Beannie's Sign Painting Service. Though the business thrived right away — the guests were mostly families looking for good homesteads, or railway workers — Dougald never considered for a moment that The Enterprise House was anything more than a temporary money-maker. The future for him lay in the rich, black-brown soil. Every day late in the afternoon, he would ride the seven miles to his homestead, consult with the hired hand, and inspect the fifteen acres he had so labouriously broken and then planted. At first, it had been wonderful, the Red Fife rapidly shooting up. But as the summer came on, he realized something was wrong: the crop wasn't ripening equally; some of it was shriveled. He realized he hadn't planted deep enough. Next year will be different, he thought.

Rebecca, meanwhile, was happy. Although the work was exhausting — she got up every morning at five to begin the breakfast and worked until supper was over at six, all the time keeping her eye, not only on Ed and Stella, but on a chamber maid who might lag for a moment — *at least I have people to talk to, and every day*. On Sunday she sang in the church choir, never mind it was of the Anglican faith rather than the Methodist she had been brought up in. She hadn't been embarrassed at all when Marguerite Black, the minister's wife had gushed, Oh your voice is beautiful, remarkable really. Rebecca had happily agreed to sing a solo verse from *Rock of Ages* at the Victoria Day Ceremonies.

It bothered her that Moose Jaw was such a hick town, but now, at least, she could laugh about it. She wrote her father: Grass as high as your knee grows along the centre of Main Street — Edward found a garter snake there the other day — so it isn't exactly Paris on the Seine. The horses and cattle make no distinction between the town streets and the open prairie so you have to be on the lookout or you'll find yourself stuck in a pile of manure.

One afternoon Rebecca discovered two women, their cheeks and lips painted a shocking red, their hair a frizzy beehive, lounging on the hotel verandah, obviously looking for paying customers. Grabbing her broom, she went after them with such ferocity — Whores! Tarts! Harlots! Not welcomed here! — that they never appeared again. *Yet in some ways they fascinate me. I even envy them. They are free in a way I'm not.*

Moose Jaw may have been primitive and rough but at least it was a society of sorts. Rebecca felt nothing but dread when Dougald announced at the end of September that it was time to return to the farm. The government regulations required that they live for six months each year on their homestead. They would obey the rules to the very letter, he insisted.

The winter was so savage that it was talked about for years afterwards. The wind never ceased groaning, the temperature dropped to minus thirty-five for weeks on end, the whirling snow seeming to blot out human existence. Rebecca was benumbed with fear and resentment, hardly speaking a word, mechanically going about the tasks that might make her children a little more comfortable. Her only relief was in itself a near tragedy.

Word came that Marguerite Black's little girl had pneumonia. Only four months before Dougald and Rebecca had stood with other mourners as the Blacks' newborn son had been lowered into his tiny grave. That their daughter's life was now in jeopardy seemed too cruel, *even for so cruel a place as this*.

The two women had become close friends so Rebecca was dispatched to the rectory to help. For days they hardly slept, keeping kettles full of boiling water for the steam, administering the mustard plasters, heaping blankets on the little girl who was cold as ice one moment and drenched in sweat the next. Rev. Black's contribution was to intone long prayers of dread over his sleeping daughter. Rebecca was amazed when Marguerite finally snapped at her husband, "If you can't do anything practical, please leave!" He had slunk out the front door and didn't return until late at night.

One day the child began breathing easier. She slept through an entire night and the next day woke up asking for gruel with brown sugar and milk. The two women fell laughing and crying into each other's arms.

It was not until the end of February that Rebecca finally returned to the farm. Dougald was amazed, and overjoyed, at the change in her. At the same time she was hugging the children and joking with them, she had bussed him on the cheek. Almost an accident it seemed, but to Dougald it didn't matter. Any little warmth was a relief from unbearable resentment. Even Rebecca was surprised at the flush in her own cheeks. *Maybe it's a promise of pleasure to come...*

By the first week in March the weather had turned mild, the snow almost melted. Dougald said it was time that he went to town to prepare The Enterprise House for the coming season. Still concerned over the homestead regulations, he insisted that Rebecca and the children had to remain on the farm for another month. But, he promised them, the trails would soon be passable and then they could come to town whenever they liked.

The day after he left, the snow began falling. Since there was no wind — Rebecca thought the tranquillity quite sublime — she wasn't overly concerned. Looking out at the silent white prairie, she even saw some beauty in the big, puffy flakes — *Like a bride's bouquet playfully falling from heaven.*

Even after three days of never-ending snow, she still wasn't frightened; Dougald, as responsible as ever, had laid in a mountain of provision and in the little hut near the back door was stacked plenty of wood.

Then overnight the temperature plummeted. By morning a treacherous surface of ice had spread like tin plate over the white prairie. When Rebecca stepped out the door, her foot broke through the crust, the shards badly scraping her ankle and calf. Underneath, the granulated snow was so deep it seemed to Rebecca like perverse quicksand.

By evening it was thirty five degrees below zero. The children, already bundled in layers of clothing, were wrapped in blankets and put to bed. Since she didn't dare let the fire go out, she wrapped herself in a quilt, and sat dozing by the stove. At close to midnight there was a loud banging at the door. Though frightened, she didn't hesitate to open it — there was something too desperate there. Standing in front of her was Timothy McNally, the closest neighbour to the Carmichaels.

Rebecca had taken an instant dislike to him. *He is a dandy, with his silly little mustache and such fine clothes.* Of delicate build, he had green eyes that were at once devious and seductive and a British accent that taunted everybody. Dougald thought he might be a remittance man: He certainly knows nothing about homesteading, hasn't even brought his tools. How he thinks he's going to survive out here is beyond me.

It was the Carmichael brothers who ended up doing most of the work building his hut until McNally took it into his head to quarrel with them.

He had come across what looked like to him an abandoned shack out on the prairie. He had confiscated the few goods inside as his own, then torn it apart and taken the wood to build a cooking shed. Dougald Carmichael was furious: That is William Bennie's place, where he lived in the summer when he was seeding and harvesting. He's working on the railway right now to make a few dollars, but he'll be back. And where will he go in the dead of winter? Tim McNally had simply smirked at his anger.

Rebecca had been desperate for neighbours — *If that's what you can call them when they live half a mile away.* But she had hardly seen anything of Betsy McNally. Expecting her first child, the young woman had stayed at Marguerite Black's house for her laying-in. By the time she and the baby girl had moved out to the farm, harsh weather ruled out casual visits.

Rebecca quickly pulled Tim McNally into the house, sat him in front of the stove, poured him a hot cup of tea. What she would always remember about that moment were his strange emerald eyes — *They were bulging so horribly I thought they were going to fall right out of his head. He was shaking like a soaked cat, could hardly get the words out of his mouth.* He finally managed to tell the story:

It snowed so heavy we couldn't get the door open. In a few days our food was almost gone — we were eating mush, wheat cracked same as you give horses. The baby never stopped wailing. When the snow stopped and it was calm, I thought, well, I'll go and get supplies. But then that terrible cold came and I knew I hadn't left enough wood.

McNally began to cry, quietly at first, but the sobbing grabbed hold of him, then intensified until his entire body seemed consumed with agony. Finally he let out a wail of such anguish, such utter, unrelenting fury, that it would haunt Rebecca's dreams forever.

Dougald finally arrived home the next morning. While it was his duty to immediately confront the tragedy, it fell to his wife to make the preparations.

The scene was not as repulsive as Rebecca had imagined. The young woman's hair, long and fine, was splayed on the pillow like golden thread in a medieval tapestry. Her childlike body was curled in a question mark, her thin hands delicately embracing the infant who was lodged in the V between her knees and belly. *A Madonna and child beautiful and eternal. Sacrificed to a foolish man's dream.*

The stiffness had already set in and Rebecca knew that she did not have the physical or emotional strength to attend to the bodies. *Somebody else will have to see to it. Not I, not for anything.* She could tell Dougald was disappointed in her.

She did go to the burial. It was a warm, almost hot, day, and the mourners felt dragged down in their heavy wool coats. The snow had pretty well melted and the graveyard had turned into an expanse of thick, gummy mud. As clumps of dirt were thrown on the casket and as Rev. Black muttered desperate prayers in the bright sun, Rebecca made a pledge to herself so powerful she felt it settling into her very bones: *I will escape this place. What I must do and whom I must sacrifice matters not at all.*

Dougald was determined to expand his farming operation that spring and had made a whole string of important decisions to that end, made them alone, because, although he tried to talk them over with Rebecca, her eyes quickly dulled. He had traded in his reliable old oxen, Ring and Coon, as Ed called them, for two sturdy Clydesdales which, he figured, would cut the planting time by a quarter. He planned to break a further twenty-five acres of virgin prairie which would mean planting a total of forty-five. He promised his family: This is the year the wheat will grow so tall, so lush we'll think we're sailing on a golden ocean.

He made a deal with his wife. He wasn't interested in operating The Enterprise House, but if she'd take over as manager, he'd do the necessary repairs and shingle the roof.

It was Rebecca who cleaned it, from top to bottom; the rough pine floors were bleached almost white from her scrubbing. But a week after the hotel opened she realized business was not going to be nearly as good as last year. The railroad workers had followed the construction west; there were fewer homesteaders arriving — *The word's got around what it's really like out on that prairie* — and three other entrepreneurs, hoping to copy The Enterprise's success, had opened similar establishments. These had an advantage of being located closer to the train station — travellers were so exhausted from their long voyages they were eager to fall into the nearest bed.

Rebecca did not give in to despair. She knew the other places were fly-by-night operations — and, indeed, one closed down only a week after it opened. If she provided the best home-cooked meals, and kept the place spotless, she was sure The Enterprise House would not only survive but become a flourishing Moose Jaw landmark.

She lavished attention on the guests that did come her way, preparing crockery pigs with corked snouts that, filled with boiling water, warmed the beds, serving lemonade and cookies in the parlour, placing cut flowers from her magnificent chrysanthemum bushes on the dining room table. Still, by late August, business was so slow, that she reluctantly decided to take her husband's advice and close down for the season. *It'll be much better next year. I know it.*

Dougald was determined to make life as comfortable as possible on the farm and to that end he had used their shrinking savings to improve the shack. He and his brother had laboriously dug out a cellar and then reinforced three walls of the house with cement. A kitchen had been added, with two windows, a door on hinges, a floor of poplar boards and a roof that had two thicknesses of elmboard with tar paper in between for protection in the winter. He argued with his skeptical brother: Surely she'd realize that life can be civilized even out here on the prairie.

Once back on the farm, Rebecca did try. She made curtains of red calico for the windows, with a matching dress for a delighted Stella. She pinned up several pictures of Bern, Switzerland, from a rotogravure her father had sent her. She polished the beastly commode till she could see her face in its surface. In the evening while Dougald watched the children, she took long walks out on the prairie. She had to admit that her husband was right: the wheat had shot up unbelievably lush and heavy. It was just beginning to ripen — the scarlet of the sunsets intensified the dazzling yellow. *It will soon be the gold of Dougald's dreams and I must try and love it.*

Rebecca liked to get up before everyone else, relishing the few moments alone. Before she tended the fire, she would step outside to embrace the colours of the dawn. One day in early September she awakened particularly early. She felt a sharp chill so she put her old wool shawl around her shoulders. Outside, her eye caught a mysterious sparkle of light and she walked towards it. With horror she realized instantly what it was: over the water left out for the pigs shimmered a thin layer of ice.

It was Dougald who had to confront the devastation. The wheat that only the day before had been standing so straight and strong was now blackened and misshapen, row upon row of wasted soldiers ravaged by some cruel enemy. For perhaps the second or third time in his life, he cried real tears. The odds are stacked against any ordinary man like me taming this capricious land, he wailed to himself. The ghosts of this place are laughing at me.

Yet, somehow he managed to pull himself together. There was enough left in their savings, albeit just barely, to provide provisions for the coming winter. But they'd have to do without comforting things like brown sugar, baking soda, chocolate. For just a few months. Rebecca could feel her stomach twist.

She might not have acquiesced if she hadn't received such good news. Her reputation as a superb cook and meticulous innkeeper had indeed been established. Colonel McNair of the North West Mounted Police Detachment asked her if she could prepare a gala Christmas dinner at The Enterprise House. There had been a near mutiny among the ranks — the men were sick of the loneliness and primitive living conditions — and the colonel thought a day of celebration was exactly what they needed. Their families might even come and visit.

Rebecca planned for the event all fall. She sent her husband out looking for the bushiest evergreen tree, she wrote her father asking him to dispatch ribbon and crepe paper, she ordered, on credit, all the ingredients for the dinner, including an exquisite desert she had concocted the year before — apple-jelly tarts of a red and green colour for Christmas.

Dougald tried to be as helpful as he could. It wasn't so much that he understood that Rebecca was doing what she wanted — she would soon grow tired of the tedious work involved in running a hotel, he was sure — but the Colonel was digging deep into his pockets, and the Carmichaels badly needed the money.

In the second week in December, Rebecca, taking little Stella with her, moved into the hotel to ready it for the guests expected that week. The previous fall, a bakery had opened next door — Rebecca had not liked the proprietor at all, a fat Irishman who smoked a cigar even as he was mixing the dough, and who always said something crude and lascivious to her. Now she noticed with disgust that the odour from the place, strangely sour for a bakery, permeated through the walls of The Enterprise House. *Thank God the aroma from the cooking goose will blot out that nauseating stink.*

By December 18, she had just about completed the decorations, bows of spruce everywhere tied up with ribbons, festive loops of red and green crepe paper, some holly she had managed to get her hands on. Exhausted, she had gone to bed with her daughter beside her, and fell into a deep sleep. It took a long time for her to realize that the child was desperately trying to shake her awake.

The smoke was already very thick but Rebecca had the presence of mind to grab the hammer and smash the nearest window. She and Stella had just crawled through when The Enterprise House exploded. *Like a festive firecracker, like a Chinese lantern, like a catastrophic bloody explosion.*

The baker tried to blame the disaster on Rebecca, claiming that an overturned gas light had set the evergreens aflame. Dougald said this was ridiculous; the blaze had obviously started in the bakery ovens. The two men were close to punching each other when the Rev. Black intervened. Since both the hotel and bakery were nothing more than smoldering ruins, he pointed out, what good would their arguing do. The Carmichaels returned to the farm.

Fortunately, winter hadn't yet arrived; the temperature hovered around a balmy thirty degrees. Rebecca, however, was frozen in silence, inanimate, as though her world had been obliterated.

Dougald hoped that the holiday might relieve the terrible gloom that now lay over his household. On Christmas Eve he had taken the last of their savings and had bought a few small gifts: for Stella, a little Dutch doll with wooden shoes, for Ed, a set of soldiers, and for Rebecca, a nice bottle of eau de cologne.

In an attempt to cheer his wife up, he organized a Christmas trip to town. They would attend the church service — Rebecca was to be the featured performer, singing several verses of *Oh Come, All Ye Faithful* solo. At Rev. Black's invitation, they would lunch at the rectory.

But on the morning of the holiday Rebecca steadfastly refused to go, whimpering of stomach pains, *the female complaint*. The desperate pleas from Stella and Ed did nothing to change her mind. Dougald said they would, of course, stay with her. *But I want nothing but to be alone, you could give me no greater gift than that peace*. Dougald realized he had no choice but to grant her wish.

The Carmichaels enjoyed themselves. The church service was inspirational, the decorations lovely, the music, even without Rebecca, thrilling. And Marguerite Black was so gracious. Ed and Stella filled their stomachs with candy and plum pudding.

It was four in the afternoon when they finally set out for home. The sky was a leaden gray, a bitter, strong wind had come up, snow was just starting to fall. The house was very quiet when they arrived, but they were used to that. Ed hurriedly clomped in, anxious to tell his beloved mother about their adventures. His holler of alarm swirled in the embroidery of snow: Some madman has smashed our place to bits with his ax.

Actually it was only the commode that had been attacked; bits and pieces of rosewood, engraved brass and gilt were flung everywhere, one door had been ripped off, another swung from its hinges. The claws had been savagely hacked off. Ed imagined he could see blood flowing. Poor beast.

The three stood frozen in disbelief until they heard the alarming wail and rushed outside. Standing atop the roof, her dark hair whipping in the wind, her arms outstretched to heaven, Rebecca was belting forth *Joy to the World*. In years to come Ed would recall nothing but the deep shame he felt. Stella remembered that she thought her mother looked like one of the lovely angels that had decorated the church. Dougald too always thought about the unearthly quality of that moment, but what was etched in his mind like acid on glass was the patch of pitch black, the curly hodgepodge, that covered the most private part of his wife's anatomy.

*** *** ***

The following fall, after Dougald Carmichael had finally enjoyed a decent harvest and hope was again in the air, he received a letter from his wife. He was embarrassed when he collected it at the post office — Just like her not to hide anything, he grumbled. The return address was plain: c/o Blackstock Asylum, Blackstock, Ontario.

Dear Dougald:

It has been a beautiful summer here. In the little woods nearby, Trillium, their pretty white faces a perfect Trinity of triangles, blossomed early in the spring, then the Lady's Slippers, scandalously purple, sprung up like circus clowns...

Roger Morier

Roger Morier is a Canadian writer, journalist and broadcaster who lives in Paris, France.

SON AND MOON

I kick the loose pebbles at my feet one last time, pull the jacket's corduroy collar closer against the November chill, and stare out across the ancient ramparts into the still valley.

In the orchard below, the mulberry trees have lost most of their broad leaves. Their limbs hang nearly naked against the dark, brooding flank of mountain just across the way. On the valley floor, the silver glint of a clear stream disappears into the next valley, crossing the Cevennes from west to east.

These are some of the oldest mountains in France, they say, part of the Massif Central, that high-level and largely barren plateau which slices the country in half, separating north from south. Here at the edge of the village, when the sky is cloudless as it is today, you can see more than 50 kilometres, all the way to the rim of an extinct volcano, the one more and more tourists come to explore these days.

The silence, like the immense blue sky, could be terrifying. At first you don't realize it, but after a few moments it is impossible not to notice the presence of this absence: no trees rustling, no birds chirping, no wind whistling. Eerie almost, but perfectly normal for an isolated village high in the Cevennes at the approach of winter.

The village itself lies on the crest of a hill. At this time of the year, in the long shadows of a late afternoon sun, there is a certain harshness in the air — the gnarled chestnut trees, the cold, sharp fences made of grey slate slabs lying high upon each other, the charcoal coloured houses, square and imposing.

Or at least what remains of the houses. Here, too, time has worked its wrath — just two houses stand complete with walls and roof. The dozen or so others are in the same condition as the house where my grandfather once lived — roofless, one or two walls half collapsed, a few shards of glass jutting out from window frames, small piles of rubble on the inside of what used to be a home and a hearth.

When my grandfather left here many years ago, before the First World War, he guessed that he would probably never return to see the house, and he never did. He left behind brothers and sisters, family and friends. They all thought he was mad because, when he left, he jauntily told them that he wanted to "marry the century".

They didn't quite understand just what that meant, thinking he was putting on airs again, and they told him so. But he left anyway, followed the sun, and they never saw him again. Nobody in the village did. He had heard a different call.

The silence of the valley must have weighed heavily on him, as it surely does on anyone who lives here. Or rather, as it did on anyone who used to live here. For this village, like thousands of others in rural France, exists no longer, save only in the minds of people like me, a descendant of those villagers of another era, come on a pilgrimage, searching for sources.

This morning, I met the only person who is still a resident. With the help of a cane, she was making her way haltingly along what used to be the principal pathway amongst the houses, an elderly woman with a lined face that seemed older than age. She was thin and frail, a bird really, with a simple black dress over black woollen stockings and black shoes.The shock of pure white hair under a shawl only emphasized her penetrating blue eyes. *Madame* was out for her daily walk, a guardian of memories making her rounds.

"Yes, I remember your grandfather," she said, breaking into a soft smile after I had introduced myself and asked some questions. "He left here one day a long time ago. I was only a little girl then, but I still remember people saying that he was a lucky one because he was leaving. He was strong, and tall, with a thick moustache. I remember, too, that he was a stubborn fellow, always determined to get his way."

That was when my grandfather had been only twenty-one. Like all young men everywhere, he had had dreams. From his few letters and diaries, I know that his dreams had been different from others in the village. Instead of plans to start a farm farther down the valley, he had visions of some other world, where the horizon wasn't blocked by the shadow of the hillside across the way.

In the village schoolhouse, he had been the one continually in the makeshift library set up in the small corner, next to the coat rack, reading any of the well-worn books he could get his hands on. Every now and then, when it was his father's turn to hitch up the village horses and go down to Largentière for supplies for the farm, my grandfather would go with him and visit the library in the larger town, sitting and waiting there until the return trip, all the while reading whatever he found.

My grandfather would come back from those trips excited about his latest discoveries, yearning for the foreign lands and cultures which fascinated him more than he could understand or explain. It was a pleasure which he cultivated as carefully as the villagers tended their crops. Reading about places far away was one thing though; trying to imagine being there yourself was an impossible dream for a farm boy in a poor family growing up in the remote mountains of southern France.

My grandfather, then, was easy prey when Monsieur Archambault came through the area in the spring of 1908 to hold a few public meetings in villages like this one.

Monsieur Archambault was a Canadian government agent sent to these parts to recruit settlers for the new country — men and women who would populate the prairies, work the land, produce food, and, most of all, spread themselves about in case the Americans ever made good on their periodic threats to move north of the 49th parallel and take over the wilderness land.

The government was offering twenty-five acres of land to anyone who would settle "out west", as Monsieur Archambault called it. It was rich, black soil — so rich, he promised, that you just had to throw a few seeds onto the ground and vegetables would come up almost by themselves a month or two later.

Twenty-five acres. That was more than the people in this village had amongst them combined. Chasing forlorn sheep across pastures or labouring to make grapevines grow in the rocky soil was a terribly hard way to make a living. One of the poorest regions of France, the area had remained a backwater in the country's 19th century drive to industrial development.

To be sure, Lyons wasn't that far away in the adjoining Rhone

River valley, its silk factories the heart of a thriving industry which depended on mulberry orchards in places like this little village. But the orchards were owned by others in distant Paris or Milan and the people in the village merely worked them. The wild prices paid for those luxury textiles never trickled down to those who actually shepherded the silkworms and stood patient as they spun their dense cocoons, the strands of silk destined for the back of wealthy matrons somewhere far from here.

My grandfather had thought it all so unjust, this painstaking work for such little reward. When he heard that so much land was there for the taking, and when he learned that the government of the Dominion of Canada would even — yes ! — pay his voyage to claim the property, he knew immediately that his days in the village were about to end. He knew, too, that he would have to explain this to his mother.

"You know what you are?" she said when he had spoken excitedly about Monsieur Archambault. "You are the dark side of the moon."

"That's an odd thing to say. What do you mean?"

"I have seven children, but you are the most distant, the most mysterious. Just when I think I understand you, you say or do something that makes me wonder if I really know you at all. My own son. Hmnmn."

I know that my grandfather had been hurt by that remark. It's not as though he had hidden his intentions. He had always told people about his love for travel, even though he had never actually done much of it, and about his desire to leave the village, to see a landscape which contained something other than a mountain face across a valley.

"Why do you want to leave?" continued my great-grandmother, probably knowing that her argument was already lost. "Here, you have the family, our home, the village, all that you want."

"Maybe, but over there I know that I'll find what I need."

The conversation turned cold, as my grandfather had expected it would. His path, he knew, lay before him, and things went quickly after that. Over the next two days he prepared his bags and made the rounds of all his friends and family, saying *au revoir*, planting kisses, promising to write, suggesting in a joking way that they come to visit him in the new world, knowing full well they never would.

He left early one Tuesday morning to walk the seven kilometres downhill to Largentière, from there hitching a buggy ride to Nîmes, and then, with the ticket which Monsieur Archambault had given him, on to the steam train which took him to the Atlantic port of Bordeaux. In the port area he was met by another Canadian government officer with a bright smile who distributed more tickets to the group of men like him, all destined to board the next boat heading to Canada in three days time.

Of those three days he spent in Bordeaux, my grandfather left no trace. I know only that he departed for the new world, landing in Halifax, then getting on a Canadian Pacific train which a week later would see him arrive in Winnipeg.

From there, it was another buggy ride to a small, isolated village some 50 kilometres to the south, on the way to the border with North Dakota. And from that village, he was taken by another smiling Canadian government agent seven more kilometres, again on foot, to a parcel of land covered with thick spruce trees. There, in a small clearing, the agent showed him a small, brown canvas tent and said proudly: "This is yours."

Alongside the tent were some tools: a pickaxe, a saw, a hammer, and a rake. Some food — flour, salt, lard, carrots — had been placed there as well, and my grandfather noticed a nearby artesian well as a water supply. After that, there were a few brief words, a hearty handshake, and the agent was gone. All was quiet.

I think of that scene from time to time, but never more so than now as I stand in what remains of the village where my grandfather was born, kick the loose pebbles at my feet, and stare out across the valley.

Under the broad prairie sky in the spring of 1908, the silence of that clearing in the spruce trees must have been as impressive to my grandfather as the stillness of this Cevennes village and valley is to me. He was alone in the solitude of his thought, with no mountain flank across the way, facing an endless horizon as flat and unbroken as the Atlantic Ocean he had just crossed.

What must have gone through his mind at the moment, I wonder, as the government agent left him on his own, so far from what had always been familiar. Was he satisfied to have reached his destination, finally able to put his meagre belongings down in one spot, to contemplate a landscape he had only ever read about in a far-off mountain village? Or, for a 21-year-old peasant lad from high in the Cevennes who had just crossed a country, an ocean, and half of a continent, was he terrified at the enormity of what he had accomplished and what still lay before him?

Unlike many his age, my grandfather had made a real effort to set down his observations and impressions when he lived in the French village, but he lost the desire to do so when he arrived on the prairies. Months later, there were letters describing the new land and his new life. Those first few months, though, have been erased, as if the immensity of that flat land and its interminable stillness snatched from the man the very words he could use to describe it. As if, to accompany the enveloping silence, he lapsed into a mutism to which he was not accustomed and from which he would only slowly emerge.

I never knew my grandfather. He died years before I was born. But I remain inspired by his undertaking, awed by his courage.

As I think of him and try to imagine what it must have been like at that time far away and long ago, with no boundaries before him and no end in sight, my seven-year old son suddenly runs up and tugs at my sleeve.

"C'mon, Dad, you said you'd play Lunar Stalker on the GameBoy with me."

Lunar Stalker. It is a sudden lurch away from thought, a call to the present. Instead of imagining the birth of a Manitoba farm almost a century ago, I now face the existential angst of my son revolving around the year 2121 and whether the good guys will manage to defeat the bad guys. On the far side of the moon.

My son has never been to a Manitoba farm, never seen the infinite space of that wide open country. The voyages he prefers are made inside a small plastic box with a dot matrix screen and stereo sound.

As I watch his intense concentration and his fingers as they fly across the GameBoy buttons, I can only hope that someday he, too, will feel the need to push back the horizon, to get out from under shadows, to explore lands far from these abandoned mulberry pastures and empty villages, away from this country he calls home.

Maybe he'll go to Canada. As voyages occasionally come full circle, maybe he'll search out what remains of his great-grandfather's farm, centred on a clearing among the spruce trees, not far from the U.S. border, under a wide, blue Manitoba sky. I know that he won't grieve for the past because the past doesn't exist, it is only in the mind. Maybe, though, like me, he'll wonder why the most revealing journeys are sometimes those to the heart.

Joanne Page

Joanne Page is a writer, poet and artist, whose publications include *The River and the Lake*. She was editor of *Arguments with The World: Essays by Bronwen Wallace*, has written as a columnist for the Kingston Whig-Standard, and has written poems for several periodicals. She lives in Kingston.

one half of a correspondence

May 3

Dear Jan,

What I saw when I met you:

Anticipation the nub of it, a person positioned so as to be ready for a lifetime embellished, the buttery yellow dress I later learned you chose so you would look a daffodil in April, official flower, settled in a room among welcoming women, and when I asked how you were doing you made mention of

these travails that flesh falls heir to and a person felt compelled to ponder what variety of storage bin lies in that cranium of yours painted in crayon colours like the bed linen you showed us in the Sears catalogue, stuffed with a grist of arcane expressions, legal preamble, stray formula from the periodic table, blackthorn cudgels, items to keep at heart as these next months unfold and you sort what is necessary

out from among time remaining.

This letter is only to say that I hope to spend time with you and pursuant to that

be delivered into your corner
with supplies for the haul

to the height above the sun
 where the firmament reserves its absent light.

July 21

Dear Jan,

Breathing space.
Questionable procedures,
two days in a row seeking a fugitive in green
going downstream a little faster than the rest of us,
I find you hanging on to a guarantee never issued
under the scanner.

You grab your smile,
tiny offering in this radiantland,
Nuclear Medicine being all out of licorice allsorts,
no, the only truck or trade here is in bones, my dear,
chittering breakaway reckless bones, ivory castanets,
   scaffolding for the heart.

Sidelined temporarily in the catacomb,
subdued to who you are not,
I looked Death in the face, you say, *and He*
blinked.

Here is the exact moment for wild tulip meadows,
  for higher songbirds
    orioles in the arboreal forest crown,

cinnamon, slideguitars
         a three-day Legion dance
    chiming perfumed June
an absence of liars.

       Who would it help you to know
      in these days longer than their length,

itinerant Aladdin in resplendent silk, a festival of clowns
  or the pastry chef from Rideau Hall, why stint, who's counting
    costs, someone to make you grin, can it be so hard, can you laugh

again, may I take your hand, will I
        will you out of here?

September 6

Dear Jan,

Much to do with dying is swerve,
unforeseen douse of lakewater on hot rock,
skid.

In truth neither sorcery nor already-written scripture
will turn this autumn holy
only the laying on of solid colour,
sky thrown down behind trees, torrential & finally
blue, the divide between high ground and the galaxy,
your red hair
exclamation mark in the punctuation of crowds,
these burning white days, their edges fluted

when much to do with love is waiting
to be held,
without judgement,
including the parts you would disallow
if you could,
your friends, me,
at you to let us closer,
time running out, your body
a chorus of cells belting out a song against extinction.

September 25

Dear Jan,

After the first treatment,

today you looked not bad
which is to say that you opened the door
served me some canned soup, vegetable,
flung out the quilt, peopled further, new add-ons,
we laughed about which is permanent
who is merely glued on
& therefore can be removed at a moment's notice
at whim,
neither of us saying the obvious:
that not one of us is here to stay
and you walk as though
even the air through which you move injures,

knowing, you said, that a whole lot
doesn't make any difference,
that what will eventuate
is pretty much what's going to happen, meaning
another woman alone
at an unexpected intersection
of what is necessary
with how to take a run at additional time
& greater comfort & being sure of your kids,
sorting through medical choices
for peace of mind.
All the carrot juice in the world, you say,
won't do much more than a couple of glasses
of tapwater, won't interrupt what is already in motion,
like any mother
working in limited time for the telling.

The wind blowing restlessly

downs the first leaves,
it's a day later now.
We get out our appointment books,
undertake a prolonged discussion about food,
menus leading to a plan
and we get right down to it,
a date finally agreed on
with much describing and redescribing the location
of this affordable yet delicious restaurant
with respect to the nun and muffler places
to prolong the pleasure of having been smart
enough to pin down an occasion when five of us -
damsels, we call ourselves —
can get together, important
to peg in an ordinary minor pleasure,
critical.

Quieter, each morning a fistful of motionless trees
costumed, regal,
pillars holding apart the air and the earth
for one more day that I would wrap
deliver to you in the western
suburbs of this greystone city
full of penitents counting,
marking off their calendars towards release,
freedom the difference between cinders and gold
in a moving stream,
limit, source, the whole glittering dance.

October 10

Dear Jan,

This woman on the stage who seized the crowd by its
unsuspecting neck, Shop around, she said, check out the
sales on burial at sea & cenotaphs, each day a sheaf of
naked foolscap. Who is this woman on the stage of the
university hall wearing hair a shade too red & sculpted to
within an inch of its life, her listeners never guessing the
one choice permitted, that the story might be about
figures at the edge of the landscape, playing random
songs on a keyboard, inaccessible as the biographical
details of a harlequin.

October 27

Dear Jan,

The birthday party:
room filled up
you under your wig
in the corner chair
chosen for strategic purpose
having quilted your brains out all week
so as to have the gift
in tolerable state of readiness
changing your mind about the colours
at the twelfth hour
and making a second,
everyone commenting on the length
and distance between the stitches
a hit, a sensation, a downright wonder
considering how under the weather
you were as late as Tuesday evening.
I have to think that if you were tied up
and lowered to the depths of a forty-foot well
& left to your own devices for two days
you'd have three or twenty quilts
neatly piled on your forehead
when we reeled you back into
this company of fierce companions.

the gifts:
bag of popcorn
glass bowl broadly curved
a journal
wooden basket with apple
mobile of seedbearing plants
red clay mask
handmade table linens
work of recent fiction
bold stories

of engineering instruments
to be found in builder's supply depots
on Friday a night crawl.
This celebration unloosens
scent over tawny barrenlands,
quiet plume of air,
returns the future to a distance
between mountains,
rift valley & ungovernable flowers.

November 3

Dear Jan,

Today puts you half way.

Time left with you in it is a picture,
the picture with you in it has left time,
deserted, fled, abandoned calendar and clock
become a drumming chamber,
a heart that got toughened up by being
broken a couple of times, very heart
which will injure a crowd of others
including mine when its rumba beat hesitates,
stops. Where is the sense in the mathematics
taking you and leaving Clifford Olsen to his dreams
of children five miles to the south,
how to understand a late and lasting flourish
of polished leaves shot through with sun
as your chemicals spill, get torched, and flare wild?

November 10

Dear Jan,

breakthrough

yesterday in the blue of November's sweetest ache
downtown for treatment
me preceding the staff
determined you won't slip by
get installed in the rabbit warren
of rooms
be therefore unfindable

you turn up breathless
smile like a bullet-proof vest
I stick to you like glue.

long consultation in a room
cold enough to flash freeze
if we aren't careful,
jokes about forgot to
pay the heating bill,
you out flat on the bed
under a thermal blanket
several flannel sheets
breathing too fast
not deep enough
to rosy up your cheeks

we shift
oncologist and nurse
undo and unlayer
tapping down the spine
listening for a crackle
your back unprotected
and I want to wrap you up with my arms
make you into a temperate zone

treatment room
a glacier dispensing poison
tiny drops inside plastic vacuumed sacks
fluid into a major vessel
scarlet in your case
wild poppy red, spectral

comes ordeal first:

a white tray
surgical gloves
does this hurt, Hon?
iodine wiped on
& off
the square cotton patch
fingers kneading
sorry, sorry
needing the outline
thought we were in
pinned down
slender steel
maybe sitting up
        would be better
into your skin
hand to hand
stronghold
I don't want to hurt you
        sweetie
five times
a blessing
your blood rich
crimson fast up the needle
Yes!
and what fell away in that moment as vapour against a
wafer sun is how you've held yourself apart all these years, not
wanting to put anyone out — what you learned from your mother
who does it well, so many decades of practice, no limit to the means,

the end: protection against freefall, hurtling cliffleap into the ether —
what we do if we trust
  careful not to ask
      brush up close now
         and a feathered wing sweeps down the sky
           it's that easy

we will not speak of disappointment or foregone events
we will not tell stories we cannot believe
we will not permit useless options
we will not travel down detours or upstream
we will not learn anything but a glad song
we will not go back.

we will receive fruit at the door
and sing the lowering sun
beyond snow ridges & breakers
through the false tease of melt
into spring.

November 13

Dear Jan,

this is the night, hard breathing, pain increasing,
breathing, breathing, the oxygen on, off, pause, on, off, pause, the
cat pacing back and forth between us, visiting nurse beside you on
the couch taking vital signs, a worry: pulse up, pressure down, temperature low enough to hardly make a vertical although you maintain you are hot. you were always hot my dear.

she phones to find out how worried we ought to be. No problem,
says the covering oncologist, if she wants to be at home, that's where
she should stay (or words to that effect), thereby confirming one final
time that you are in charge and what you want is what will happen.

a fast trip for me to the pharmacy on Princess to get a morphine
prescription filled before closing time, rapid tear-streaked trip and
long wait in the near-empty store, back again to hickorywood, driving
carefully, a night for precision in each act.

you under the red and yellow quilt, waiting, nurse gone, and we get
one of the pills into you, pronto. Pull up the drawbridge, you say, and
I grapple with the uncooperative locking mechanism of the front
door, leave the keys on the kitchen counter. We settle in for Scarlet,
Episode One, between puffing breaths, your struggle for oxygen fills
the space between us, occupies the room, is the only sound in the uni-
verse, might extinguish the stars.

eleven-thirty: another couple of ginger ales, one each. I'm on the
other couch under an apricot quilt from upstairs, you are upright,
can't lie back on the pillows. I wonder how you are going to sleep sitting up. The answer is that you don't, breathing is a full-time job
commanding complete attention. Also you are in pain. Another morphine in

one o'clock: listening, breathe in, breathe out, the rhythm of the
pump, cat from your couch to mine to the window, an equilateral tri-

angle in the starlight

two-thirty: more ginger ale, ice, you are slumped forward over the two small pillows, no quilt.

three o'clock: sick, mop-up, towels. I'm dizzy, sweating, upstairs and get sick too, might as well be in this together, both of us on your couch now, I hold you.

three-thirty: sick again, I have defiled the couch, you say, in your little-girl voice, you smile, I smile, it isn't really funny. you are feeling really bad? I ask, you nod. we've got options, I say, we can call the nurse again and get some more stuff to settle your stomach. you think about that for a while, we sit still.

three-forty: I think, you say slowly, that we can't do this much longer. I want this to be your call. I don't say anything. we look at each other, your breath faster, the machine pumps on, you say:

I think we have to go.

November 14

Elegy for J. B-H

(1945-1994)

no bringing you back
    no losing you

the tiretracks scored deep
your front lawn grass held the lines for seven days
on hickorywood
unforgettable
    short-term memory

the stretcher
    going downtown
right hand turns all the way
one last try at standup
leave behind the wig & costumes, the half-finished quilt
    thread-drawn daisies
        tacked close-hauled across green sea cotton
voyaging over your dining room table
    a last gift

you planned one for me

comes it now:

    iv-drip
  my arms our words now
  your hands flutter
irregular signals
vital signs
  just get to sunrise, I promise you,
    and the worst will be over.

breathing together

you, me, the machine
labouring
our lungs
      a pair of rowers sweeping through to the final reach
your life a silvered wake overturning
turning over, each way out
behind us

you bent over your knees

this restlessness

    here it comes

        I think I'm going

in the punishing neon hospital light and deep in your eyes —
    the ivory arc of a breaking heart.

November 23

this is the last letter

Dear Jan,

I am counting scarves
wraps of primary blue swirled hue
prospects of rearrangements in the air
waiting word from immortal you, new job:
assistant head, department of revenge

large desk, getting at the paper work
stern face intent on retribution
secondary sources to be considered
pursuant to previous conversations, all on the record
few allowances will be made.

I gotta tell you it's late November, Jan
the weather remains mostly clear —
keep the bright skies coming, sweetheart,
we'll get to Christmas baking later in the month
or whenever we stop expecting your next entrance

you ought to know

those roses of yours kept blooming
in the Gardens of Babylon among the fountains &
tea rooms, the terraced levels stepped
down to the deer park known as Cataraqui Woods,

where anyone else might have considered
a couple of russet chrysanthemums for late fall
you planted briar rose
it held a good two weeks,
all that blessed oxygen possibly
seeping out, adhering

one thing though
I need your number
the matter is I miss our evening calls
your answering voice breathless
distilled to a higher note
making me think I've interrupted
a chemistry experiment
or re-enactment of a principle
of physics like centrifugal force,
your kitchen spinning
coconut shreds pasted to the walls
macadamia nuts
earrings and chicken feet slippers
quilts sailing over the western township,
wealth of soft cotton tucking the stars in
their fleet light extinguished
      the long day journey begun

      get busy with the single random acts
   contracts, proposed subversion
chains of unexplained events
  to unhitch that ex of yours
    from surplus money or his wife:

churls and cretins flung in disarray
this endpiece more than words can say.

Patricia Abram

Patricia Abram is poetry editor of *the Harpweaver*. Her poems have been published in *The Antigonish Review, Canadian Author, Contemporary Verse 2, Beyond Bad Times,* and *Fireweed: A Feminist Quarterly*. She lives in St. Catharines, Ontario.

A MOTION STILL

I remember your blue hat, netted veil
catching the brown of your bangs
and your white gloves gripping a patent purse,
mint chiclets you chewed in our white pontiac,
the ritual of sundays.

the children's room sighed a closet of
secrets and supplies   stencils and crayola,
cracks tracing the wall and
my grandmother teaching the word,
her grey hair curled into knots, her cat glasses
pointing out her fierce love for Jesus.

you perched on the pew,
your ancestry backing the family view,
your hands folded in disbelief
till the charade stopped when I was six and
we slept in sundays.

you meditate the cancer globed in your breast,
a stillness in motion.
you tell me that flux, fire, live in twig and blade,
stone and cedar, flesh,
beginning in the cell that motions   still
beyond the stencils and crayola and cracks,
a secret past the pew

and you motion still.

NESTS

Last year
under our eavestrough
a blue jay carved a nest
on a criss-cross of wires
connected to our house.
The bird gathered curls
of leaves, sticks, twists of hair,
grass. Wound them into a
circle. Finally she sat
on eggs I imagined to be
ovals of smooth yellow.
She'd fly away to collect food
for herself,
or her babies —
I wasn't sure if they were born yet.

My mother waits for the birth
of cancer from breast to bone.
Or brain.
Feeling an ache in her pelvis,
dizziness in her head,
She scratches out her concern
through telephone wires,
her worries nested to herself,
now to me.
Not my father, or sister, or brother.

Pears grow every August on
an ancient tree in our backyard
and every year the squirrels
gnaw them into orbs of cheek.
Last June as I pulled weeds in the garden
a squirrel slunk across
that wire link,
ate the globes of egg,
transparent bird flesh.

This spring my son
tells me of construction.
Another building.
He points to a nest
balancing on the same wires,
points to tail feathers striking blue
above twigs.
We watch
as the bird gathers,
sits, waits the days.
Waits.

Today the nest curls alone.
I look for the squirrel
and know the circle curves —
in August
pears will fester
like tumours
in closed mouths.

HER LIGHT

*"Within every blade of grass are enshrined
the mysteries of an inscrutable wisdom."*
            Bahá'u'lláh

My mother has cancer;
a stone in her breast they dug up,
its fine grains seeping to her blood.
Every day she sews stitches
creating quilts,
one for each grandchild,
seven in all.

She cups the cancer in her hand
like an orb of clay,
and meditates its light.
On the phone she tells me
how she flows into its shine,
leaving her body like a wisp of dried skin.
How she sinks into peace,
soft palms lifting her, the light an eye
encircling her. For ten minutes, an hour,
she travels this ray and lands like a sigh,
full, unbroken.

This light burns, she says,
in the veins of a girl with auburn hair,
in every man creased with age,

in blades of grass that slit the sky.

With fingers stiff, she sews her days,
her thread stitching light
into each quilt.

Kathy Fretwell

Kathy Fretwell is a poet, journalist, and artist. Her books *The Ultimate Contact* and *Apple, Worm, and All* were published by Fiddlehead Poetry. She has also been published in 33 journals across Canada. Born in New York City, she became a Canadian citizen in 1970, and lives near Parry Sound, Ontario.

AFTER WATCHING DR. PETER'S VIDEO-DIARIES

He disintegrates right before my eyes in a seamlessly taped video friends loaned me. No time lapse, a slow-motion continuous demise. Physician, gay, B.C. resident, Dr. Peter invites viewers to his death-watch to humanize the AIDS response. Foregrounded against the shores of the sunlit Pacific, the slant of sun through rainforest, the back curtain in an AIDS comedy benefit, the kitchen sink in his favorite niece's home, Dr. Peter shows us the downward spiral of his hopes, health, lifespan. The video's conclusion is narrated by a trusted friend. Wailing, I relive helpless rage at watching death triumph in the most gruesome way imaginable. AIDS' hitman, Kaposi's sarcoma, torpedoes Dr. Peter, lesion by lesion.

CANCER. Like AIDS victims, my family had no immunity against the various cancers which demolished them.

Cancer. Does writing about it invite the dread C inside me? Fortunately, I am not marked (yet?) by the beast which gobbled up my mother's family. Five out of five in their prime. Words cannot mirror the devastation of this microscopic organism which literally destroys a person cell by cell. Words cannot portray the terror of watching my 5'8" 160 lb. mother slowly, grotesquely, disappear before my very eyes. Words cannot paint the horror of sub-visible locusts cleaning out entire populations. These invisible grim reapers vanquish organisms thousands of times their size. This reality puts me in my place, teaches me humility toward all other life forms. Death flaunted its evil arts at me long before I could say the word.

Swallowing at age two that never-discussed horror of Daddy choking on a turkey bone Christmas '46 taught me the power of silenced fear, the sedation of gobbled chocolate. Absorbing that slow cancerous implosion of my grandmother, mother, kindred aunt, and grandfather imprinted denial, human frailty, bodily betrayal, divine helplessness, a void. Guessing at my maternal grandparents' agonized demise inscribed finality: a terrified silence shrouded each dead kin ever after. Digesting the murders of one uncle by a male date and the other by a son's kick to the heart, which preempted death by lung cancer, soured me on the North American Dream. The Dream's illusion of the good life for all spawns violence, vendettas. Facing so many deaths so young has shaped my life.

How many and how have they died. Let me count the ways. 1937, seven years before my birth, my maternal grandparents embrace each other's cancer, die within two weeks of each other: he — March 23, she — April 8. I know them only from their Obituaries, flip side of the NY Herald Tribune's Nuptials page. Fleshed out slightly in 1988 through the biased eyes of Kate, their daughter-in-law: he — convalesces during my mother's nuptials in 1934, she — is not yet stricken with dread cancer; he — brilliantly lawyers, she — scales the social peaks, but as a suffragette.

1944, I am born and Daddy, stationed in North Carolina, hops a baggage car to arrive in NYC for my first day of life. He exits my second Christmas, drunk and choked by a turkey bone. His father, world-renowned maxilla-facial surgeon, cannot catch Daddy to do a tracheotomy. Daddy runs for his life, Granddad runs after him with the carving knife - my own nursery rhyme. Back from the hospital, Mom lies to me, "Daddy's on a trip" — a trip called D.O.A. Not allowed to attend his service and burial, I conclude: "Bad, bad Miss Pooh" (Daddy's nickname for me).

At my parents' wedding, according to Kate in 1988, my paternal grandmother cries her eyes out, leaves before the toss of the bridal bouquet, hates to let her son go. In 1950, Nana falls in the bathtub, breaks her arm and breaks her heart. She follows Daddy to the family plot (again, I'm not allowed there) in Ichabod Crane's Sleepy Hollow. A cancer of the soul, insidious as the alcohol which metastasizes in Daddy, in everyone.

Six years later my favorite uncle #1 falls. Hopping between NYC and the Virgin Islands, he expands his textiles firm and his base of operations so frowned upon by society. Ignoring his son's pleas not to go out, he hits the St. Thomian night, his regular cruising bars. A native agrees to a taxi-ride, changes his mind midway to somewhere, shoves my uncle out of the speeding cab. My uncle strikes the curb, flies into a coma, then dies.

American Dreamers are strafed; they're cancroid. 1962, my favorite uncle #2 is also murdered, closer to home. Thanksgiving 1961, he toasts my mother — her lung cancer in remission — then receives Xmas early, his own prophecy of death by lung cancer in 12 months' time. He and Kate, the 1988 chronicler, continue our family's adult tradition: drunken yelling, in Pleasantville NY. His son, glutted with the fighting and the drinking, kicks him in the heart down the stairs. Cancer's victory usurped, he dies the next day, Valentine's. At his wake, the first one I'm permitted to attend, Mom rehearses her own release, as green as he is rouged beyond recognition and reproach.

The horror, the horror overwhelms metaphoric embroidery. Prior to that thankless Thanksgiving, Mom chooses my high school yearbook quote: seek the truth for it will set you free. But freedom yawns into the abyss as Mom's fast-approaching death dawns on me just before finals. The power of denial! For the bulk of that dread-filled 1961-62 school year, I block out Mom's growing emaciation, the blue gashes on her back, the weekly drainage of her lungs, daffodil-yellow eyes skin fleshless frame, dead-white hair, barely eaten baby food, sweet rotting smell. During finals, I forget to write a Bible paper (no agape no eros only thanatos, it seems, at my church-affiliated prep school). All I study for the Biology exam is evolution, the blessed ongoing adaptation of life, life, life! Mom dies two weeks before I tremble ghostly and white-gowned down the aisle for my diploma. Alone. Life is No Dream, the moon's godless arc, the sun's soulless march. My rage and terror blitz nucleus after nucleus until I'm shot through, petrified Death-in-Life. What has our family done? Why are we razed, clearcut?

Death and henchman Cancer stay away long enough for me to earn two degrees, a career, a husband. In 1969, I learn of dying well. My paternal grandfather dies of prostate cancer at 93. He's met, done, said all, he's ready. But gazing down at Mom, Daddy, Nana, now Granddad, underground at Sleepy Hollow snaps my fragile trust that life unfolds as it should. Earthbound, I lift my eyes to the cloudy skies and hear family-spirits' derision that I'm stuck below on my clipped Pegasus. Above no love.

Our personal holocaust, my aunt, lone survivor, artist like me, drunk like me. Her mother, her father, her sister (my mom), her brother — meals on wheels for cancer: trussed bodies on gurneys gobbled in no time flat. At peace her final years, she sculpts in Florida, warmed by white stucco, Persian cats, Spanish moss. When cancer gets her by the throat, her son shelters her. I visit. We laugh our linkup, cry her dying, solidify our love in art and verse. In a seven year span, I divorce, heal, remarry. The night before I find sobriety, I weep for this kindred aunt, her death in 1974.

Here ends my maternal family: grandfather 60, grandmother 61, uncle 51, mom 54, aunt 64. Labelled 'drunken loco artiste,' she outlived them all. Now 50, I exult that 3 made it into their sixties. I chant my mantra: my paternal granddad outwitted cancer until the age of 93.

I have a fanatical urgency to live every day to the full, an uncompromising and sometimes buffoonish need to show and express love, an irrational tenacity to obsess on and pursue self-expression in writing and art when far more talented people than I have given up because they know they will never be known/famous in their fields, a feeling that often lies dormant fatefully festering, a love of beauty which erupts into sobs in the most public of places such as Festival of the Sound concerts, an eidetic memory which keeps my long dead loved ones alive within me even four decades after their deaths, a diffuse awareness of death and life which never leaves me ever, a do-or-die overreaction to loss and abandonment, a fear of ending relationships — even unhealthy ones, a vibrant hatred of the lie: all-is-well-so-you-are-crazy-to-fear, a former hatred of elderly women which disappeared after healing completely with Mom 32 years after she died, a love for most forms of life — all if my phobia of spiders is overridden by the conviction that spiders are part of our interconnection interdependence.

I could rant on and on against premature death, cancer's cruel theft of kin in the prime of life. I was born prematurely in wartime NYC. Mom miscarried four times, almost lost me, then lost her ovaries, tubes, and uterus immediately after my birth. I got out just in time! Maybe cancer and I have been at war all my life. I fill my cells with spirit and light. I caress my pendulous breasts honouring them; Mom couldn't honour hers — the Fifties loathed living tissue, questing souls.

Cancer. Savage snowball dance, Mathusian manic progression. Landfill site on human skin, laboratory animal skin. Hitman always seeking an Achilles' heel.

Consumption. Ultimate consumer in our consumer world. Quintessential cannibal. Divinity's chancre. God's leather whip. Medicine's megabucks industry. Unwanted guest infiltrating the centre, the core Kore.

Cancer my Sign and Mom's anguish. Malevolent shapeshifter, necrotising flesh-eater. Trickster, you finish off what AIDS begins, capping off with Kaposi's sarcoma.

Witnessing people die, looking through wasting flesh into the bones, the soul, determines the way I look at people — needing to look beyond the skin colour size shape origin class income education sexual preference — we're talking the essence, looking beyond those externals to the phosphorescent soul, the luminosity in the bones. That's why I rudely stare into eyes/irises/lens/Third Eye deep deeper: one naked soul meeting another and all trappings, facades, fripperies fade away. Like looking up into the Milky Way, the luminous points dancing in midnight blue darker than black the heavens.

An image from Dr. Peter's video comforts me: twilight's silver-tipped wavelets, part of the infinite Pacific, keep homing in shoreward, keep homing in.

TO MY FAMILY'S KILLER

Cancer, glutton, craving
food many times your size -
you chewed through all five.
After Mom married, you polished

off her parents, two husks
ever hollower as you gorged,
<u>hors</u> <u>d'oeuvre</u> in your feast
of Mom's family. Alive to me

only in newsprint, their stories
silenced by the horror you bring -
the lingering aftertaste
of your <u>bon</u> <u>appetit</u>, their aura.

Next generation the main course,
you daintily nibbled, four snacks
on Mom alone. First you bit her womb
and I got out just in time, in my wake

the reproductive kit & caboodle.
Her breast, second helping, made you
drool for her siblings. After
Thanksgiving, you gobbled

Mom's brother. Just before my finals
in high school, you topped

off with Mom's lungs and liver,
loving the ride in her blood.

Final frontier, Mom's sister.
You supped on her palate, larynx.
Age thirty, I sobbed; we screamed
your name. Now I don't feed you

our family addictions. At fifty,
near the age of kin you devoured,
prime cuts top choice, I won't be your
just desserts or any other course.

I fill my cells with light, I fill

Uma Parameswaran

Uma Parameswaran has written *Cyclic Hope Cyclic Pain,*
Trishanku, Rootless but Green are the Boulevard Trees, and *The Door*
I Shut Behind Me. She has won the Canadian Authors' Association
Annual Fiction Competition. Born in Madras, India, she lives in
Winnipeg, Manitoba.

CANCER SIMPLE AS A FLOWER

"How can he say such a thing? 'cancer simple as a flower'?; a flower, why a flower? does he think cancer is beautiful? or innocent? or natural? what else does a flower mean to you, Maru, tell me. Cancer simple as a flower, yeah flowers die fast, I guess that's what it is, huh? And he's supposed to be a great poet, huh." Lynne threw the book off her lap, and slid downwards on the hospital bed and pulled the sheet to her face. "So why do you think hospital beds are never placed along the wall? isn't one supposed to turn away and face the wall just before one dies, like cowboys are supposed to ride off into the sunset?"

"You read far too much, Lynne," I said.

"Never has been a problem so far, so why now? I've been on the Dean's Honours list from day one, I was supposed to do my Master's at Cambridge, remember, Rhodes scholarship, all those references from my profs you typed up for me?"

Lynne was our best Honours student in the last ten years. As English department secretary, I had been typing references for students for a decade and there had not been another Lynne MacAlister in my time — straight A+ in nineteen of the twenty courses. More important, I had known her for twenty years as my neighbour's kid. My little Kris and she had walked to school together from grade one to grade six, at which time we'd put Kris at SJR, a private school.

I picked up the poetry anthology and flipped through the pages. "Karl Shapiro," Lynne said. I turned the pages. There it was, with Lynne's highlighter markings. "Auto Wreck." I read it.

"You know what he means, Lynne, 'suicide has cause, stillbirth logic' but an auto accident makes no sense."

"That's what he says, but auto accidents happen because of bad drivers, drunken drivers, or mechanical defects which drivers are supposed to check for from time to time, all of which go right back to human volition. A human being DOES something, like drinking or not taking care of his car, and an accident is the deserved result. But cancer? what have I done? how could I possibly have prevented it? I've never smoked, never afforded the luxury of tanning my skin on beaches, never had reason to use contraceptives. I've never even used tampons, for godssake. There's absolutely nothing I could have done to prevent it and nothing I can do to stop it. There's nothing I can do, period, except die soon and get out of this mess."

She was referring to various types of cancers but not her own. But she was right. She had not done anything wrong. I took Lynne's hand and stoked it, starting with the fingertips and gently working upwards. Lynne was angry. But that too was a defence mechanism, for the alternative was depression and loneliness. Everything had happened so suddenly. She had gone into the walk-in clinic with what appeared to be a minor problem and a week later was in hospital, diagnosed with cancer; now, six months later, she was back in hospital, awaiting surgery.

"My aunt Chittammai had breast cancer in those days when we didn't have all these cures."

"The aunt about whom you have so many stories?" Lynne got interested. "She died of cancer?"

"She died in time, as all of us must," I replied, "but she managed to do a great many things before that. Like saving the cow that had cancer. Want to hear that story?"

It was perhaps my voice that did it; I didn't speak in low tones or with fake joviality (we'll get you out of here in no time) as her other visitors had, but in my usual anecdote voice, that she had heard over the years during the times I had been in a babysitting pool with neighbouring mothers.

"That's not a question but an Ancient Mariner grip, right? holding me with your glittering eye. I'll have to hear no matter what." Lynne was more relaxed already, and teasing me the way she usually did.

"You remember where Chittammai lived? in this big house on an acre of land right in the middle of Bangladore? that had been built there before the city had grown around it?"

"Yup, I remember, where you used to get monkeys visiting every summer? remember the time a little monkey died and all the monkeys kept a vigil over it all day? tell me that story again."

"Some other time. Today it is about Gauri the Cow." It was something about my motherly figure and voice that almost made Lynne settle down twirling her hair with her left hand, the way she used to in her childhood days of afternoon naps.

"Chittammai had hardly returned from the hospital after her mastectomy before she fell near the steps and broke her ribs."

"Oh no!!!"

"She took that too in stride, there she was in a wheel chair, all bandaged up, and running the house at full throttle as always."

"With all those domestics and gardeners and chauffeurs."

"But the only thing she couldn't do was laugh, because of her ribs."

"She had a hearty laugh for her petite body, right?"

"A+ for your memory, Lynne. One day, Muttha, the man-of-all-work, brought a cow from their estate — they had a country cottage, you remember? just outside the city, where they had fields and several cows and bullocks. The cow had a tumour that had grown to the size of a pumpkin in the three months that Chittammai had not gone to the estate, what with her surgery and ribs and all. The farm hands had made the poor cow walk all the way to the city because she was so ill. So there she was, tottering into the yard, and before the vet could come, right before our eyes, the poor thing flailed out her legs, each outwards, and crumpled to the ground, right there under the jackfruit tree.

"The vet came, took one look at the cow, and shook his head. Bad news, he said, when a cow does that, falls that way, all splayed out, there's nothing can be done, as good as dead, sorry ma'am, not a chance, no point doing anything either, throwing away good money after bad, sorry ma'am. And away he went."

"Oh, what a jerk," Lynne said, now quite into the story.

"Aren't you glad your doctor isn't like that?"

"Sure am, but go on, what happened?"

"So Chittammai asked the chauffeur to go across town to bring another vet, he was chief of the Government Vet Hospital, way across town. She told Muttha to bring the stoutest, longest ropes he could find in the store room, and get four men from the cigarette-shop across the street, where servants from nearby houses congregated. Then she wheeled herself to her room, and came back with her medicine chest. It was a large wicker basket, one of those things one took for picking flowers. She took out all her vitamin pills — she was on B12 and A and C and D and calcium and iron and what not — had Muttha grind them all together, mixed it with molasses, and then had him shove the mush of vitamins and molasses into the cow's mouth. Two men had to pry Gauri's mouth open so he could place the mush ball in her cheek.

"The cow was too weak even to swallow and so she lay dribbling at the mouth. Then Chittammai had the men pull two ropes over a branch of the jackfruit tree near the cow, had them ease one end of each under the cow and make a knot so they could pulley the cow up and adjust her feet the way they should be under her, kind of standing but supported at the same time by the ropes. Chittammai went to the cow, stroked her and spoke to her. And after about twenty minutes, the cow started slowly moving its mouth, chewing the mush."

"You're kidding, right?"

"It happened right before my eyes, don't ask me what the story means or how it relates to your poem or you, but it did happen. The vet was not in town, but the cow turned for the better and of course the tumour was duly operated on."

"Don't tell my doctor any of this," Lynne laughed. "He wouldn't let you come within reach of me. Just mushing all her medication into a ball and stuffing it into Elsie's mouth, I can see it. Wow, I'd have liked this Chittammai of yours, what made her think of all these things? the ropes, what an idea!"

"I asked her that, and she said it was a Friday, and she wasn't going to have the poor cow die on her on a Friday, goddess Lakshmi's day."

"Maru, you've lost me, what's this superstition?"

"I guess it is no use trying to get anyone to understand, but had it been Thursday, she'd have said she wasn't going to have the poor cow die on Hanuman's day and if it were a Monday, that she wasn't going to have her die on Siva's day and so on, Devi's day, Krishna's day, Kartikeya's day. We just have something special on every day of the week through the year to tell us we shouldn't let anything bad happen on any day without putting up one hell of a fight, simple logic, right?"

"You think you could come by again and tell me more of these odd-ball stories, Aunty Maru?" She hadn't called me "aunty" for at least six years, grown out of it as children do, and I felt tears choking me up. But I could also feel Chittammai at my shoulder, and I knew all would be well. And so it turned out to be.

William J. Thomas

William J. Thomas is an author, scriptwriter, radio commentator and nationally syndicated newspaper columnist. His books include *Malcolm And Me — Life In The Litterbox, Dancing With The Four-Armed Man*, and *Hey! Is That Guy Dead Or Is He The Skip? Curling And Other Stories I Wished I'd Never Written.*
He lives in Wainfleet, Ontario.

HOW I HELPED MY MOTHER FLUNK HER SHORT-TERM MEMORY TEST

I'm not sure if my mother is losing it or simply executing a clever and devious plan to send me up to the Clarke Institute of Psychiatry in a caged vehicle and wearing a white jacket that laces up the back. Very tightly.

My mother Margaret, the Mighty Mick from County Cork, is now 89 years old. I'm 49 years old. Spending a lot of time with her as I have over the last ten years, everybody says I now look her age.

I love this woman but Lord knows, it ain't easy.

For instance, last month I got a message to get Margaret to a doctor's office for a test at 1 p.m. My mother lives with my sister Gail in the city of Welland, Ontario, and the hurried instruction I got on my answering machine gave me only the address of the clinic, a time, and the caveat: "Urgent!"

Gail and I are trying to get approval for a home care program in which a lady will come to the apartment a couple times a week, spend time with my mother and then leave with a really bad headache.

So at 1:05 my mother and I sit down with the local geriatrics specialist. It's the first time I've ever not spent an hour waiting to see a doctor, so I'm already a little suspicious. The doctor has no idea what kind of test he's supposed to administer because of course the family doctor who did the referral, didn't forward the paperwork yet.

"So what's wrong with her?" he asks.

"Well," I begin, "my mother is 89 years old and has arthritis in her hands and one knee gives out now and then. She's been in two car accidents which have left a bump on her head and pain across the shoulders. She has an artificial hip and cataracts cover one eye."

I swear to God he looked directly at me and said: "Has this caused her any problems?"

I turned around to look behind me to make sure he wasn't talking to someone else, perhaps an evil phantom son who whispered: "It's only a hangnail Doc, she's a chronic complainer."

So I said: "Well, you know she's had to quit playing hockey in the Welland Industrial League."

He did not smile, smirk or sneer. I am not making a word of this up — he shuffled some papers, looked over at my mother and said: "You know, at your age Mrs. Thomas, you shouldn't be on the ice."

My mother is oblivious to all this because she still prefers to wear her $400 hearing aid in the change compartment of her purse. (This is actually kind of neat because when you really raise your voice to talk to her, all the loons on her one dollar coins put their wings over their ears.)

"I'm just going to ask your mother a few questions to test her short term memory," he says.

This is not good news. Believe me, if my mother ever went on Jeopardy, the last thing you'd ever hear her say would be: "I'll take Short Term Memory for 50, Alex."

"Mrs. Thomas," he begins, "What's the date today ... what day of the month is it today?" Then he repeats the question loudly.

My mother looks up at the ceiling, then down at her shoes, then realizes he's preoccupied with making notes on his papers so she looks over at me, shrugs, and mouths the word "eight?"

I give her a blank stare. She gives me another inquisitive nod and silently says "eight?"

It dawns on me that my mother is asking me to help her cheat on her short term memory test. My biggest fear is that if I help her, she'll finally figure out how I managed to get through college.

It occurs to me that I've known the doctor all of six minutes while I've known my mother most of my life. "Six," I mouth back.

"It's the sixth today," she says.

"Sorry, it's the fifth," says the doctor, making a note. My mother looks at me, shakes her head and gives me that "I can't believe you got through college" look.

My mother is just now learning what I knew as early as grade five

— never cheat on a test from a person that's dumber than you are. After all these years I still hold Stinky Sawchuck personally responsible for my two-year residency in grade 4.

"What year were you born, Mrs. Thomas?" asks the doctor as he returns to his file.

My mother looks at me, and nods inquisitively. I hold up five fingers and a thumb. "Six," I mouth. She shakes her head, side to side. It's like my mother is a fastball pitcher and I've just given her the curve ball sign. I can't believe it, my mother is shaking me off.

"Six" I say in silence, and hold up six digits. She hesitates, thinking I'm still working on that "day of the month" question.

The doctor looks up.

"It was about 1906," she says.

The doctor looks at me because he doesn't know the answer.

"Close enough," I say.

The doctor nods at my mother and says, "okay".

As he looks down at his notes Margaret gives me the thumbs up sign.

I can't take any more of this. It's too ridiculous. If I start laughing uncontrollably I just know he's going to ask me to take the test, next.

"Look I have to pick up some groceries, I'll be back in a half hour," I say, as my mother shoots me a look of betrayal.

But before I can close the office door she says: "Don't forget the bananas."

Right. If the short term memory test involved bananas, bran and Sleeman's Lager, my mother would have aced it by now.

About a week later we got word that Margaret's home care application had been approved.

When I picked her up to bring her out to my place at the lake for a few days, the first thing she said to me was: "I guess I did pretty good on that test, eh?"

"Yeah," I replied, "you did just great."

There was absolutely no way in the world I was going to try and explain to my mother that you have to fail the test to successfully qualify for the home care program.

Frankly I just couldn't take the sigh, the shaking of the head and the look that says: "That's why this country's in trouble — college kids."

Timothy McCartney

Timothy McCartney is a nom de plume of a Canadian journalist, author, and broadcaster.

ENLIGHTENMENT

Laughing in spite of his despair, Norman Freestone stood on the hilltop, shaking his fist at the dark, storm-tossed sky. Laughing, because he remembered the stories from his youth about how many things of religious significance happened on hillsides — the delivery of the ten commandments, the appearance of angels to shepherds, the Sermon on the Mount. So this, his choice of locale for his confrontation with the God he no longer believed in, was a deliberate geographic irony. Rather clever, he thought.

Norman also didn't believe in angels. He wasn't sure he believed in shepherds! He laughed again — quite a good sense of humour for a man who was being smothered by the cosmic complexity of it all. Quite the wit. Quite the ...

He *had* always believed in science. Actually, he had always believed in what he, a completely unscientific thinker, had assumed to be science. And it was science — via one of those new television "teaching" channels — that had taught him that people who are struck by lightning feel tingling precursors to the final bolt.

So Norman would have been very surprised indeed, had he been alive for even a second or two after the lightning surged through his body. But he was not.

That particular hill was actually the seventh tee on the Forest Green Golf and Country Club's back nine. Early the next morning, the regulars arrived, ready to jostle — in a pleasantly social sort of way — for the right to tee off first. But today, George McKillop had beat them all. It was just as well; George was heading out to play a fast 18, alone.

His fellow members were relieved to see him leave the tee ahead of the pack, because most of them, on other occasions, had had the misfortune of preceding Mr. McKillop, thus offering themselves up as unwilling but almost inevitable targets for his fantastically long but desperately erratic drives. They had all been victims of his lack of patience, as he drove too soon, hole after hole, threatening the physical and mental health of all in his path, in his haste to complete his solo 18 in the two hours he had before his morning sales meeting.

George hated those sales meetings, but he needed his job. How else could he pay for his membership at the Forest Green Golf and Country Club? But, if the truth were known, as it wasn't, certainly not at the club, George's job wasn't going very well. Not well at all. He had what in a large corporation would be called a cash-flow crisis.

He was flat, busted broke.

His frustrations seemed to render his drives even longer, but even more erratic. On two occasions on the front nine, he hit the green with his drive — but the wrong green. Green six on his second drive, and green eight on his fifth. Any golfer will appreciate the intensity of his emotional upheaval when it is revealed that he actually played a five-iron off this eighth green, creating a second and considerably deeper hole approximately four feet south-west of the original cup.

Worse still, when he swung a mighty stroke on the seventh tee, his ball took off at a 45-degree angle, straight for the corresponding seventh tee on the back nine.

He found his ball lying four inches from Norman's body. A slight indentation on Norman's jacket indicated that George had actually hit the dead man with his drive. He had hit lots of live fellow members while playing through, but he had never before struck a deceased stranger.

For a moment, George believed he had killed the man, but he quickly ascertained that Norman was stone cold, although he still smelled of smoke, a little like a billiard room around 6 a.m.. Besides, powerful though his drives were, George doubted that their force would partially incinerate an accidental recipient. Norman's face was certainly ashen — but then, so was George's.

George had never been alone with a dead body before. His first thought was to run. His second thought, which kicked in before the first one made it from his brain to his legs, was that he had at least 10 holes before anyone arrived here, and maybe there was something good that could come out of this rather odd situation.

This train of thought was inspired by the diamond ring Norman wore on the ring finger of his right hand. Norman was not poor; he was just cosmically confused.

George was shocked at this unbidden idea, but not too shocked to wonder what Norman might have in his pockets. And to realize that if he acted quickly, he could reappear over on the ninth fairway of the front nine, finish up half the course, and call it quits for the morning, apparently ignorant of this tragedy on the back nine.

He gingerly lifted one side of Norman's unbuttoned coat with his seven iron. He slowly reached in, and extracted a wallet from Norman's inside coat pocket.

Norman, although in despair, had a finely honed sense of the dramatic. His thinking had been, if he were going to confront this non-existent God, he should do it fully armed, as it were, with all his worldly goods — at least, those goods conveniently available — on hand. So he had brought along $15,000 cash, just in case (he had chuckled, with only a hint of hysteria) God wanted to bargain, or asked for some kind of bribe.

George knelt, transfixed. Fifteen grand. Fifteen thousand dollars. Not enough for a private jet, mind you, or a Caribbean island, but a considerable boost to a guy in financial trouble.

Within six seconds, he had decided to keep it. Within 14 seconds, he had become convinced that this was God's way of helping a poor man out. In fact, he remembered with sudden clarity, he had invoked God's name only three holes back, when he was in that sand trap. Not in the most reverent terms, he would be the first to admit, but clearly God was very broad-minded.

George pocketed the cash, shoved the wallet back into the inside coat pocket, and decided to leave the ring. Minutes later, his chip shot landed on the ninth green of the front nine, only inches from the cup.

His day went well; it was, without question, the best day George had had in months, maybe years, maybe ever. His encounter with the late Norman Freestone had been replaced in his mind by his Encounter With God. George realized that he should do something about this; he felt the call to respond to such divine benevolence. He would take action on his way home. And he knew just what to do.

As he stepped out of the front door of his office building, he saw Malcolm Allsopp.

Malcolm was distracted, a bit dazed, and very confused. He was wondering if his wife, Edith, really meant all those things she had said, and he decided she probably did. Especially the part when she said she'd be damned if *she* was going home to *her* mother, so he could move in with his mother, instead. And when he had tried to point out that his mother had passed away, years before, Edith's only response was "And lucky for her!"

He had to admit she had a point. A few of them, in fact. Even when he had had a job, he hadn't made much money. And what he did make, he bet on the horses, and on football, and — on one notorious occasion he tried not to think about but couldn't help it — on what kind of sandwich a co-worker's wife had made that morning.

He still couldn't believe anyone ate anchovy and peanut butter sandwiches.

Malcolm tended to bet on everything, including whether or not his boss would notice when he was late for work, six days running. As usual, he had lost.

So here he was, stumbling aimlessly down the street, worrying about where he would sleep that night, and where he could find a job, and other pragmatic concerns, when a stranger stopped him, handed him $1,000 in $100 bills, said, "God bless you," and turned and walked away.

Malcolm was stunned. He had no way of knowing, of course, that his anonymous benefactor would use the other $14,000 wisely, apply himself to his job with rejuvenated dedication and energy, and achieve a modest level of financial success until the day, eleven months later, when he would be electrocuted in an unfortunate incident — never satisfactorily explained — involving a short circuit in an automatic teller.

In an entirely different way, Malcolm Allsopp, too, was shocked. Not so shocked that he forgot to shove the money in the most immediate pocket to get it out of the sight of strangers, but shocked, none the less.

"God bless you." It must be a sign. Things were going to be all right. They were going to be great! His luck had turned!

A thousand bucks was not enough to solve all his problems.

Malcolm was clear-headed enough to realize that. He intuitively understood that God was giving him a stake; it was up to him, now.

Malcolm usually travelled to the racetrack by bus; today, it was too urgent. He took a cab. He handed the cabby $100, and grabbed his change. As the taxi drove away, he discovered the cab driver had made a mistake, and Malcolm was now $10 up on where he had started. Holy cow! He ran like the wind to place his bets.

A quick look at the list of horses running in the next race — and there it was. "Heavenly Blessing", number six. He might as well have been given written instructions, signed personally by God. He put it all on Heavenly Blessing, going off at 15 to 2.

A long moment later, Malcolm leaned on the rail, limp in disbelief. Heavenly Blessing had finished seventh. The horse was never in it, not for a moment. The only reason the animal didn't finish eighth was because there were only seven horses in the race.

Finally, Malcolm eased himself upright, and headed out the front gate of the racetrack. He knew he had no place to go, so he paid no attention to where his feet were carrying him. Darkness fell, and — appropriately enough, he thought — it started to rain. By the time he had walked far enough to raise blisters, he found himself in a park-like area. He stumbled up a well-manicured, moderate incline, and stopped at the top.

Life! Ha! What a joke! he thought. What a divine riot! What was God, some kind of cosmic clown? Laughing in his despair, he stood on the hilltop, shaking his fist at the dark, storm-tossed sky.

You might think Malcolm was toying with fate, but anyone who watches those science shows on TV knows that lightning never strikes twice in the same place.

Sheila Martindale

Sheila Martindale has been Poetry Editor of *Canadian Author* since 1982. She is also the Canadian Editor for *Bogg*, a US literary publication. She has written seven books of poetry, and is the author of one play and numerous articles and reviews. She lives in London, Ontario.

RENOVATIONS

Mix the cellulose filler with water
to a creamy paste
- soft enough to work with
stiff enough to hold

With a putty knife
press the mixture
into holes and cracks

Remove excess
with a clean scraper
allow to dry

Sand with a medium-grain paper
until smooth

Brush away the dust

Paint

My walls are almost perfect
the filler is always right
- never sloppy or too hard
I work deftly and fast
to fill in all the damaged places
to smooth over the rough spots

I apply high-quality paint
its egg-shell finish looks fragile
but is in fact quite durable
and can withstand heavy use

No one guessed
the structure was in danger
of collapse.

FOOL'S GOLD

Gruff mountain man
prospecting for gold
- for four years you have sifted my streams
sunk exploratory shafts
into my core
glimpsed the elusive amber
sensed the solid ore
between the seams

And yet
you have staked no claim here
- packed up your temporary shelter
and moved on
leaving untapped the motherlode
dreaming of more prosperous fields
invisible over the next peak
reaching for the illusion of fortune
grasping the flashy glitter
of fool's gold.

SURVIVORS

Almost like old times
women gathered around tea and wine
discussing our men, our offspring
the state of our health

This time there are new wrinkles
and more than a few grey hairs
Now, as well as our homes
we talk about careers

But still it is our personal lives
which engross us
What interests us the most
is relationships
- marriages past, present, and possible
then men we left behind or who moved on
our children, mostly grown, some gone

We are strong, we women
survivors of shipwrecked lives
who have not drowned in self-pity
or clung helplessly to flotsam
or succumbed slowly to the undertow

Nancy, three years into a new marriage
and still on honeymoon

Valerie, just short of one degree
already embarked on another
while her ex works on younger live-in
number three   or maybe four

And Aileen, who has blossomed
since unloading the remnants
of her dead marriage
looking wonderful

Crystal and I share
anecdotes about ashes
- she keeps Manfred's handy
and talks to "him" sometimes
Promises herself the satisfaction
of flushing his remains down the toilet
if the memories of his manipulation
and philandering intrude
on her rebuilt life

Susan and Diane laugh
bemoan the fact
they have no stories
of divorce or death
But they also struggle
over rough roads
try to avoid the potholes
which can disable the unwary traveller

We are strong, we women
We have traded security for growth
earned no medals
for combat or endurance
paid a high emotional price
for whom we have become

And, oh, what we have learned!

Edna Staebler

Edna Staebler is an author, journalist and cookbook writer. She is
well known for her *Food That Really Schmecks* series, and has also
written *Cape Breton Harbour*, *Places I've Been And People I've
Known* and her most recent book, which she edited, *Ruby's Letters*.
Edna, who lives on Sunfish Lake near Waterloo, Ontario, was
inducted into the Order of Canada in 1996.

IN CONVERSATION ABOUT
MARGARET LAURENCE

Edna Staebler was a close friend of Margaret Laurence. As her contribution to this book, "Close to the Heart", Edna enthusiastically agreed to this exclusive interview with Paul Knowles.

PK: Tell us about your first meeting with Margaret Laurence.

ES: In 1969, Margaret was still living in England, but she was spending a lot of time in Ontario, as writer in residence at the University of Toronto. While she was there, the University Women's Club in Waterloo invited her to come as guest speaker. The club could not afford to put her up in a hotel, so I offered to have her stay with me, here at Sunfish Lake.

I had never met her before, but I knew her books very well. I had read *The Tomorrow Tamer*, and *The Prophet's Camel Bell*, and *This Side Jordan*, before I knew anything about her at all. I had started to read Margaret's books while she was living in Africa. I remember thinking, "This is wonderful writing, and it's by a Canadian!" I was really impressed. So when I knew she was coming here — and was going to stay with me — I was excited. It was a great thing for me.

When I met her at the station, I saw this woman in khaki-coloured jodhpurs, which I thought looked a little odd. She laughed about them, and explained, "These are my lion tamer pants." She changed out of them at the home where we had dinner, and put on a kaftan, a long, loose, flowing thing that Clara Thomas, a professor at York University, had made for her. That was what she wore to the hall, where she was to speak.

The meeting was open to the public, and there were a lot of people there. As we entered the hall, Margaret grabbed my hand. "Oh, Edna, hold on to me. I'm just so nervous. I hate talking like this."

I was surprised, and I answered, "You have your speech all written out. You just have to read it."

She said, "I know, but I'm just so scared."

Normally on these occasions, the guest would speak for about an hour, and then answer questions. Margaret spoke for 15 minutes. Here's this huge crowd expecting an evening with Margaret Laurence, and she spoke for 15 minutes. Then she answered questions for ten minutes, very carefully, no longer, and that was the meeting. That was it.

They always had coffee and goodies afterward; we had them pretty early that evening. We went back to the home of the couple who had hosted us at dinner. Our host offered liqueurs; Margaret said emphatically, "I'd like a double Scotch!"

We soon left their home, and drove out to my cottage on Sunfish Lake. We started to talk, and we didn't stop until four o'clock in the morning. This was just at the time in her life when she and her husband had separated. They had been apart before, and had gotten back together again, but this time he wanted a divorce. She was pretty shattered. He wanted to marry a Dutch woman, and Margaret said she thought this was a good idea, because the woman didn't speak much English, and therefore wouldn't upstage him.

I had gone through a similar marriage break-up six or seven years before, and that gave us a lot of common ground. By four in the morning, we were bosom friends. We talked very intimately and confidentially. She told me a lot of things that I have never told anyone, and never will.

The next morning, she returned to Toronto. I don't remember how long her term as writer in residence at U. of T. lasted, but before she left there, she returned to visit me on a couple of occasions. She did not drive, and she didn't have a car, so she didn't come as often as I would have liked or, I like to think, as often as she would have liked.

Eventually, she went back to England, to her house that was called Elm Cottage. She invited me to visit her in England. I was unable to go at that time, but we wrote to each other. My letters from her are now in the archives at the University of Guelph.

PK: Obviously, your friendship blossomed very quickly. Were you at all in awe of her, at the beginning?

ES: I was really quite thrilled that she would want to be my friend. I felt very humble with Margaret, because she was something very, very special, and I was just a literary journalist. I also had my first cookbook, which was very popular and sold a lot of copies, but it wasn't going to put me into the literary hall of fame. It was wonderful for me to think that a person of her stature would enjoy being with me, and that we had so much to talk about. She would listen to me as avidly as I would listen to her.

PK: Speaking of your first cookbook, *Food That Really Schmecks*, did you cook anything special for her?

ES: One time when she was staying with me, I invited some people for dinner. I made a spaghetti casserole. I made it the day before, because the recipe called for it to sit overnight. But when it came time to put it into the oven, I thought it looked as though it needed a little more liquid, so I added some tomato juice. While we were talking and having drinks in my living room before dinner, I smelled smoke. The room suddenly was filled with smoke; the dinner was running over in the oven. It was a real mess, and I probably didn't make things any neater as I ladelled off the excess liquid.

However, the casserole tasted good. Margaret talked a lot, she was very entertaining, and we all enjoyed the meal.

That recipe's in the book. And it's a good recipe, I like it, I often make it — Betsy Brubacher's Spaghetti, page 126 in *Food That Really Schmecks*.

PK: Margaret wrote about her time at your home, didn't she?

ES: Yes, in *Heart of a Stranger*. My copy of the book is inscribed, "Edna, with love, Margaret Laurence". She wrote:

"Kitchener and/or Waterloo. I never did discover which part of the town was which, or what to call each. Two towns have merged, but both seem to maintain their separate identities. This is Mennonite Country, and in the markets on weekends you can buy homemade

sausage and cheese. I visited a friend who has lived there most of her life, and who writes about the Mennonite people, their customs, their cooking, and more than anything, their life-view, which is to us amazingly untouched by this century, amazingly simple and related to one another. Naturally, outsiders tend to regard their way of life as archaic, but sometimes one wonders if their view won't endure longer than ours.

"Morning came early in this country just outside Kitchener, and I got up despite my hatred of early rising, drawn by the sun on the snow. I tramped along the paths beside Sunfish Lake, thinking that people in Canada really ought to be told that not everywhere does the winter come like this, with this brightness of both air and snow. Through the woods, tangled in among the bushes, a small river tried to take its course, and flowed despite the ice, making bizarre carvings on the frozen parts of itself. Back at the house, looking out the window, I saw a whole contingent of red cardinals, coming for the bird-seed my friend put out. Arrogant crimson feathers, sleek against the snow. I never imagined that I would be much of a bird-watcher, but there are moments when one is struck with a sudden intense aware-ness of the beauty of creatures, and wishes their continuance could be guaranteed. I would like my grandchildren, when they exist, to be able to see cardinals like these."

PK: Were you able to visit one another more, after she returned to Canada?

ES: Yes. In fact, during her final months in England, I thought she might become my neighbour. She wrote to me that she wanted to come back to Canada to live. She didn't know where to settle; she wanted to live in Ontario, and she thought she might want to stay near here. But she also had friends and connections near Peterborough, and she bought what she called the shack — it was really a prefab cottage — on the Otonabee River near Peterborough. I visited her there.

All through this period, she was working on *The Diviners*. She wrote it all by hand, in scribblers, and she wouldn't let them out of her sight. Whenever she went back to England, she carried them on the plane.

She worked on *The Diviners* for quite a long time, for years. When I visited her, we talked about the book.

She said, "People are going to think this is an autobiography. It's not, but I could call it a spiritual autobiography." It wasn't a factual book, it wasn't her life, or what she did. She sent me the book when it came out, and I recognized so many things — the cottage on the river, the old man next door, so many things that were familiar. She had drawn on those things. There were many factual elements in the book, but the story of her life wasn't the story of Morag's life.

When I visited her at her cottage, she would have made a big pot of stew. It would be all ready, so she wouldn't have to spend time making a meal while I was there. We just sat and talked. And went out in the boat — she had bought a row boat with money she received through a Canada Council grant for her work on *The Diviners*.

An old man lived next door; someone very much like him is in *The Diviners*, as the diviner. There was a garden at her cottage; at least, the people who owned it before her had a garden, fenced in with chicken wire. Margaret called it her weed garden, because she didn't bother with it.

The cottage was not very big. There was a fair-sized living room-kitchen, and two or three bedrooms. I only saw the one I slept in, which was quite small.

PK: Margaret Laurence was important to you as a friend, and also as a colleague, is that right?

ES: Oh, yes. When she was writer in residence at the University of Western Ontario, I visited her there. She was staying at the apartment of a professor who was on sabbatical. I remember we shared a bottle of wine; I don't drink very much, but the bottle was empty by the time we went to bed. Once again, we talked until all hours.

I asked her who her friends were, and she said, "They're all writers." I was so impressed with that because, at the time, I'd been a journalist, and I knew the editors at *McLeans*, but I didn't know many other writers. Through *McLeans*, I knew Pierre Berton, who has been my friend for life; and I knew Bill Mitchell, who is also still a dear friend. I'd spend weekends with the Mitchells in Toronto, and Bill and I would read our stuff to each other and talk a lot about it.

But through Margaret, I felt I was inducted into what she called "the tribe". In 1971 or so, when the Writers' Union started, Margaret was one of the initiators. She invited me to come to the opening conference in Ottawa. I met a lot of other writers, and for the first time I really felt as though I was part of the tribe.

PK: When you spend those long nights in conversation, did you talk about your writing?

ES: Yes. She liked my book, *Cape Breton Harbour*. I remember telling her how much time I spent writing the descriptive passages, how I spent maybe an hour on just one sentence. I lamented the fact that those are the parts that people skip when they read the book; she said, "I don't. Those are the parts I read carefully."

At that time, she was on the board for the Canada Council, the board that decided if you received grants or not. She thought I should receive a grant, and she knew I would get it, because she would recommend it. But I didn't feel I should have one, because I didn't need it, financially, and I didn't think I should take it if I didn't need it. So I didn't apply.

But I notice, when I go through the book of Writers' Union members, that different ones say, "Canada Council Grant" or "Ontario Arts Council Grant", as if it were a prestigious thing. I suppose it is, and maybe I should have taken it just for that. But I didn't think it would be fair to take money that was always scarce, when people needed it and I didn't.

PK: Did Margaret Laurence make a lot of money from her writing?

ES: I don't think she did. I asked her how many copies of *The Fire Dwellers* she had sold. She said, "Edna, I never know how many, I only know how much." And I thought, "Oh, how gross". But I later found it was just the same with me, after I started getting royalties, because you get a cheque, and you remember how much the cheque was for when you put it into the bank, but I don't remember how many copies have been sold.

PK: What made Margaret Laurence a good writer?

ES: She was a very intense person, and very observant, and she felt things very deeply. She remembered things well, and I think she felt a compulsion to tell her stories.

There is nothing glib about her, or her work. It's not brittle, or "clever"; it's deeply felt. She was a very emotional person, and it's all there. Her work seemed to me to be a true extension of her person. Her physical features were very dark. People kept asking if she had Indian ancestry. I asked her, and she said, "No." But people were always wondering. She denied it so vehemently that you wondered if it were true. She talked so much of being Celtic, of being Scottish. This was very, very strong in her, the Scottishness of her background.

She was tall, and big-boned. She wasn't a little, delicate sort of person. She looked like a strong person, and she was a strong person. She had very strong ideas.

One area where she didn't give the impression of strength had to do with her children. She was always very concerned about her kids. The last time she was here, she was expecting her son to come to visit, and she was so nervous, so scared that it wouldn't go right. She told me, "If one of my children dies before I do, I don't know how I would ever, ever get over it." It didn't happen that way, of course.

And there is an interesting footnote. I never met her children, but after my most recent book, *Ruby's Letters* was published in 1995, her daughter Jocelyn wrote a wonderful review in the Globe and Mail.

PK: Was Margaret a religious person?

ES: Oh, yes, she really was, but not in an organized sort of way, not church. She never talked about it as a separate thing; her spirituality was just a part of her. We never sat and discussed it, ever, but I know she was a profound believer.

PK: Was she a happy person?

ES: On the whole, no, not really. Although, she loved things, and she loved people, and there's always a great deal of happiness in being that kind of person. But she had this dark, Celtic melancholy, and I rather think she liked to have that. It came out at times in our marathon, weekend conversations — which always included a bottle of wine — when she would become melancholy. It was at those times I learned her favourite song was "Amazing Grace." That inner melancholy also comes out in the books, certainly in *The Diviners*. It provides a rich, brooding atmosphere in the books, and I think she rather cherished that.

She did seem to enjoy her fans. Once when I visited her at her last home, in Lakefield, I remember Margaret saying that she had 73 letters to answer. She got a great deal of fan mail, because she had so many admirers. She answered her fan mail. So do I. But she had let it pile up to 73, and that was going to be a real chore.

I think she found happiness in writing. She enjoyed it. It carried her right inside whatever she was creating.

And yet, she sometimes found it very hard. After *The Diviners*, she told me, "Edna, this will be my last novel. I don't think I can do it again."

She subsequently came to Kitchener to speak on behalf of a peace organization she was part of. Unlike the first time I met her, on this occasion she gave a long, moving speech, to a full house in a large auditorium (The Centre in the Square) and she was given a standing ovation.

She said she had agreed to come to Kitchener only if she could stay with me. So after the meeting, she came here. She told me she had been trying to write another novel, but it just wasn't coming.

"I've torn up hundreds of pages. I just can't do it." She spoke with despair.

This time, she was not writing about anything that touched her own life. The book was to be about immigrants to Canada, completely away from her own experience.

I said, "Why don't you write like you have in your other books; they all have elements of your own life, your own feelings, in them. Why don't you write about your marriage?"

She said, "I've thought of that. I think I could. But I just don't want to bring Jack into it, to do that to him."

That novel was never completed. She did write her autobiography, which was published after she died in 1987.

PK: What was Margaret Laurence's best work?

ES: I find that hard to answer. To me, they're all so intimate, so real, there's so much in all of them. I liked *The Jest of God*. *The Fire Dwellers*, I didn't like quite as much. *The Prophet's Camel Bell*, I really liked that book. Of course, *The Diviners* was such a big, profound book. She sent it to me, and I read it immediately. I want to read it again. I've read *The Stone Angel* several times, and now that I'm 90, I admire and marvel even more at its insights.

PK: What were your thoughts when she died?

ES: That it was so much too soon. I thought of all the conversations and letters we had shared about writing, and about all manner of personal things.

And even though she is known for her dark, Celtic nature and her profound books, I thought about Margaret's sense of humour. I don't mean that she told jokes; I simply remember laughing, laughing a great deal whenever we were together. She enriched my life, and I'm eternally grateful for having known her and having been able to read her books.

(Quotation from Heart of a Stranger *by Margaret Laurence. Used by permission of the Canadian Publishers, McClelland & Stewart, Toronto)*

Janis Rapoport

Janis Rapoport, a literary and television editor, writes plays, poetry and fiction. She is the author of *Within the Whirling Moment*, *Jeremy's Dream, Winter Flowers, Dreamgirls*, and *Upon Her Fluent Route*. She won the American Poetry Association Award for Outstanding Achievement. She lives in Toronto.

FROM THIS TIME FORTH
AND FOREVER

The glow of the sun and the moon and the stars
disappeared with the unravelling
of celestial harpstrings into shadow.
Then darkness sheltered in the umbra of your eyes

And death was your interpreter,
from this time forth and forever.
Your life was a tapestry, threaded with hope
and happiness and the colours of pain, and desire.

Our lamentations — mixed with laughter —
slowly gather into the fibres
of remembrance. Yet laughter is always heard
further than weeping.

With us are family and friends
who stood parallel, in rows,
as we left your grave,
plucking our few knots of grass.

We pour water over our hands, each one
setting down the pitcher, just as
we shovelled the earth, disconnected:
may the loss that began with your death there end.

We sit next to the ground, dust
on our feet and in our hair. We have ripped
our clothes instead of gashing ourselves,
counting your good deeds by our tears.

During the meal of condolence we are silent
as boiled eggs sealed inside their shells. Mouths
close around lentils that turn over in throats:
small, endless wheels of joy and of sorrow.

Our grief ripples into the concentric circles
formed by a stone flung onto water.
In the flame of the candle nearby: illumination
your wisdom brought to our lives.

Do not look for your body's reflection
in these mirrors, so recently covered.
Perhaps it is only such glass
that separates our worlds.

Let us offer a prayer brought by angels,
as the weave of your life is now spun
into the memory of children, bearers of your dreams,
from this time forth and forever.

Elisabeth Harvor

Elisabeth Harvor is the author of story collections including *If Only We Could Drive Like This Forever* and *Our Lady of All the Distances*. Her first book of poetry is *Fortress of Chairs*. In 1991, she won the League of Canadian Poets National Poetry Prize. She has taught at Algonquin College, Concordia University and York University.

NOT MY BODY

Not my body
In a wood box like a
Florist's box for a woman's body,
Laid out on puckered air,
Puckered satin,
Nightgowned white legs a
Pair of cold lilies
Decayed in their stem,

But fire,
Ashes!

Not an ash tree to
Bow over my ashes,

But a poplar tree —
That leafy clatter,

Each round leaf
A cymbal,

Jouncing and
Dancing and

Slapping itself
Against wind

Not a date carved in stone,
But these incised words of
Stony instruction:

What she learned but
Had to keep learning
Over and over again:

Not to panic,
Not to look at the
Sorrow of another and
Convince herself that,
Given the same sorrow,
She could do better,

Not to take herself
To doctors and say:
"Here is my body,
Do what you will
with it."

May she
Rest in Peace

Ellen Stafford

Ellen Stafford is author of *Was That You at the Guggenheim?*, *Stratford Around And About,* and *The Flamboyant Canadians.* She has been an editor, a book reveiwer and a bookstore founder and owner. She lives in Kingston, Ontario.

AMONG THE LILIES

The day for her mammogram. Towelling herself dry after her bath Nancy remembered — she'd been through this once before — she was not supposed to use any bath oil, bath salts, perfume. Not even deodorant (Oops! Too late — she'd already used it.) She remembered now because last time, six months ago, she'd driven in to Vancouver and apologized to the lab technician: "Hottest day of the year; what a day to have to go without deodorant!" One looked for things to make jokes about, trying to stay on the lighter side, having this test.

"We compress because we care," a notice in the X-ray room. Earlier, a friend's account had filled her with dread: "The most excruciatingly painful thing I've <u>ever</u> experienced. Torture!" Consequently expecting the worst, Nancy hadn't found it after all to be so very terrible. You couldn't say it was a pleasant experience, but she'd been relieved to find it tolerable; not the hideously painful ordeal she'd been led to expect. Unpleasant, certainly, but not even as bad as the dentist's chair and far more speedily over with.

Bath oil and deodorant. So much a part of her daily ritual. She should have written a note to herself the night before <u>No bath oil. No deodorant.</u> Postpone the appointment? No. She'd go. If they sent her away and gave her an appointment for another day, she'd accept that (with some sense of relief, of reprieve, probably). Keep the appointment. Six months ago they'd had some doubt about the X-ray. "Have another mammogram in six months. Don't forget!" She was moving away, to another city. She hadn't thought about it much. Surely if anything ominous had been found, they'd have reported it to her doctor, her doctor would have told her. But her doctor had only said something about shadows, some thickening of the tissue, couldn't quite see ... Be sure to get another mammogram in six months. Don't forget. She had a new doctor now, but she hadn't forgotten.

Hadn't forgotten — which was not to say she'd worried. With the disruption of moving she'd let it fall into the background. And "If there'd been anything, any cause for worry, they'd have wanted a biopsy," her new doctor told her. "No panic. It's just that the X-rays were unclear." Probably nothing, then. Her breasts, those full breasts that had all her life been an embarrassment, were large and lumpy. Some scar tissue in one — an abscess, a surgical scar, faded with time. Whenever she'd undressed with a man — for a man — she'd been sensitive about that. She made a point of mentioning it ahead of time, not to offend at a crucial moment.

Boobs. Bazooms. Tits. Melons. Things, parts, separated from the woman herself. Men's exuberant comments about a woman's breasts. Do women go about appraising, leering, giving the slow whistle to a man's crotch? True, it would be unfair to judge the man from what his pants reveal. Or conceal. Was it fair to rate a woman by her breasts?

In the great love of her life she'd been lucky. Those breasts about which she was so self-conscious were no problem. Unlike most males — many males, too many males in our starlet-dominated latter-day braindrain, he had no breast-fetish; he saw all of her and liked everything she was. Even her breasts, by then sagging. Once, leaving a theatre with friends, he cheerfully berated one of the men: "Hey, stop looking at those. They belong to me!" She was delighted, those breasts always her secret shame. Seeing photographs of concentration camp inmates, naked — such degradation, to have nothing to cover those breasts, to be seen in her nakedness, a small thin woman with disproportionately large breasts. Her long-ago husband had been pathologically jealous, even of a doctor examining her; she on the other hand hated the doctor looking at her because of that skimpy body, those non-conforming breasts. When she read novels by some aging male authors she felt some of that humiliation, some implied criticism of her in eulogies about deliciously upturned mounds and nipples standing at attention. In fitting rooms, trying on brassieres, she felt profoundly humble, unconsoled by the saleswoman's cheerful reassurances: "You should see some of the women who come in here ... !"

There was still the humiliation, baring those breasts apologetically for the mammogram; though perhaps she ought to be grateful that something about their shape — or shapelessness — made the procedure less painful for her than it was for so many. Standing with each breast in turn spread upon a ledge, plates at either side closing in, tightly clamping. "Can you bear that? Can you breathe? Okay now — hold your breath ..." and the picture taken. Again — this time laterally, the plates closing in from above and below. Now the other breast... Waiting then while they checked to see that the picture was clear. Last time they'd had to repeat the process, oddly enough not on the breast with the scar tissue but the other one. That surprised her. She'd always thought that if any trouble came, it would be from that surgery. Not so, apparently. Some thickening, a shadow; they weren't able to be sure. Have another test in six months. Don't forget! And so today.

And what a day! A day like this — too early for spring but a spring day, warm as summer. She drove to the hospital exhilarated. Let out of the jail of winter. Spring break, and the the students were out; fossilized mounds of dirty snow crusted here and there still, but students lounging on porches with beer. At an intersection she waited for a couple of young women to cross, one of them wearing a long cotton dress, a sundress leaving arms and shoulders bare. She smiled at them; unable to resist the impulse she called out to them, "Hooray for summer!" The girls turned to stare at her; they didn't smile back. The light changed and she had to drive on without explaining herself: "Summer dresses again — so good to see you ..." Ridiculous old body she was becoming. Those girls probably hadn't heard what she said, all they knew was that some crazy old woman in a car had yelled at them. And if someone had called out to <u>her</u> from a car stopped at an intersection, what would she have made of it? Sorry, girls — it was the sunshine, the joy of seeing people out without winter coats, scarves, boots; the intoxication of this break in the winter doldrums. Like emerging from a plane in February and finding yourself in Mexico on a summer day. Foolishness. Better watch it. Next thing, they'd be putting her away somewhere. Not without cause.

But such a day! What wouldn't you give for a day like this, what wouldn't you pay if you could buy it, if you could summon it up, order it: "One perfect summer day, please. How much?" "What's it worth to you?" "Whatever — I'm in no mood for haggling. I can put it on my Visa." A merciful break, a sanity-saving break. School children out, lawn chairs hastily dragged out of winter storage; people out inspecting lawns, checking winter's depredations, oiling lawnmowers soon to be returned to service. Her heart singing as the birds were singing. Siren song of the equinox. A little reward for long winter sufferings, a blessing, an encouragement: cheer up, folks, we've almost got it made. Almost there!

A technician in her sealed-off space was exhilarated, too. "I'm so glad you're early. After I finish with you, I'm going to take my kids to the park." (No problem about the deodorant, "as long as I know.") Adding then, "This machine is a new model. You will probably find it hurts more than your last one did." It did. After the plates were pressed in tightly, a screw was turned to tighten them still more. The turning of the screw, she thought in a panic flash of close to unbearable pain. Brief, luckily. "Now the other one ..." And it was over. She was free to go, and so was the technician. Out into that glorious day again.

She'd hear from her doctor if there were any problems. For now, enjoy this blessed day, this bonus, this delight. What is to be will be... Sure, she could say that now, in the euphoria of this bright, beautiful gift of a day, though she knew very well that if something unpleasant were to come about, if any malignancy — get the word out in the open — were to manifest itself, she'd be altogether less accepting, less complaisant, less cheerful in adversity. Why me, she would ask, as others had asked and others would ask. Why now? Why this torment at the end of a life? (And what would happen then? Radiation? Chemotherapy? Amputation? One breast or two?)

"One lump or two?" The gracious hostess, smiling, suspending a lump of sugar held in tongs over a teacup. One lump or two? Those heavy breasts — anything could lurk there, an evil thing growing inexorably, unsuspected, undetected. "Do you test yourself for lumps?" Well, not really.

Silly ... Awkwardly, laughing at herself, laughing at how it used to be, she tried to explain; girls taught not to touch themselves. Stories told about some who touched themselves down <u>there</u>: you could go mad, it was said, from doing that. Don't preen in front of mirrors: vanity could be your downfall. Bodies must stay hidden from all eyes, even one's own: her own mother had perfected the art of undressing under her nightgown! Breasts, back then, objects of utility; infants for the nourishment of, not adult males for the titillation of. Their prime function was not even that of pushing out a blouse in interesting places. Secret things. Her world, her times, concealed many secret things. So, possibly, did her breasts.

Beth had it. First a malignancy in one breast. They removed both of them. Just in case. Beth — so cheerful, to the very last. Nancy wouldn't be as cheerful: she knew she wouldn't. She'd bitch a lot, most likely. She'd have to remind herself to make a conscious effort not to become a pain in the neck. A pain in the breast to herself — would that justify her being a pain in the backside to others?

We live and then we die. And in between ... Silly! We live, which is the important thing. A day like this one made that absolutely clear. She was sorry she'd startled those two girls. She'd have liked to explain: "Just seeing you in summer dresses ..." Some of the best pictures, the most lasting ones, were only in the mind. Wordsworth's daffodils.

Joy. Such intense joy. A defence mechanism, this euphoria? A ploy devised by her wily old subconscious to keep her anesthetized, to calm the fears that might otherwise overwhelm her? "Knock her out with sunshine, sedate her with spring scents and portents; keep her delirious with happiness so she won't fret over what's going to hit her." Correction please — what <u>might</u> be going to hit her. Don't cross your bridges before you come to them. Never meet trouble halfway. Never trouble trouble till trouble troubles you. Trouble is a bubble. Let a smile be your umbrella. Somewhere the sun is shining. Look for the silver lining. Cheer up, it may never happen. All very well, but ... Never mind: today she was Pollyanna. Keep smiling. Hope springs, if not eternally, at least enough to go on.

If she'd known it was going to be a day like this she'd have planned a small treat for herself, a reward to follow the mammogram. She didn't go out much, didn't go out enough. In this new city, in this deplorable weather, she went out only to do her grocery shopping, to visit the library, to drop in at the bookshop, to see her doctor. The hospital, today, for the mammogram. Winter diminished her. She was frustrated by the intense cold, the sharp winds, the eternal snow piling up in layers chronicling the long months of winter. Today was a gift. She drove along the lakefront, stopping now and then, parking and getting out of her car to walk a little. She smiled at young mothers out with their children, stood aside to let runners go by, saw old men strolling peaceably, students sprawled on park benches.

A pity to leave all this, to go home and shut herself up in her apartment. Though the sun would be going down soon. And she was about ready for a cup of tea. A host of golden daffodils: she'd buy some to take home with her. Sunny flowers, take-home sunshine. She started a left just as the amber came on and heard a man's voice but intent on making her turn, didn't really hear him — didn't make out his words (as those girls must not have made out hers) until later. <u>What</u> had he said? "Watch your driving, granny!" <u>Granny!</u> Such insolence — a stranger daring to call her "granny." She'd gone through the amber, yes, but she was into her turn, too late to brake. And didn't hundreds of other drivers do that? Didn't <u>men</u> do that? <u>Young</u> men? Deriding an old woman. Would he have been so rude to a man? A <u>young</u> man? Forget it, she told herself, but it rankled. It made a blot on this day, and she resented that. Unfinished business. Not possible to stop for conversation. Like those girls. Forget it.

The super was down in the front hall. "Old Mr. Dalton," he said "He died."

"Died? Mr. Dalton?"

"This morning. Went for a walk in the park. Police found him and called us. Heart."

"How awful," she murmured.

"Just goes to show you — you never know, do you? And he wasn't an old man. We always spoke of him as old Mr. Dalton, the wife and me, but he wasn't old. Fifty-seven, that's all."

"Only fifty-seven?"

He nodded. "His brother's coming, from Ottawa. Shock for him!"

Poor Mr. Dalton. Yes, he'd seemed older — around her own age she'd have said. His apartment was on the floor above hers. She'd seen him a few times down at the mailboxes, coming in, passing on the stairs. A widower, the super had told her. A widower, lonely perhaps and possibly assuming, she'd thought, that she was lonely too. She'd been wary, afraid he might ask her to have dinner with him, go to a movie (watch television together?), two old people, each living alone. Not that he'd given any sign of being about to suggest any such thing; nevertheless she was cautious, spoke as briefly as possible without seeming discourteous. Going out a couple of days ago she'd met him coming in. "Mighty cold out there today," he said. "Need to wrap up well. Wind's very sharp."

"Is it always so windy here?"

"Pretty much, I guess. We call it the Windy City."

She made a pot of tea and took a couple of gingersnaps from the package — her secret passion. Damn — she'd forgotten the daffodils. Shaken by that man shouting at her. Too bad; she'd meant to stop for some. Poor Mr. Dalton. He might have died just as she was having her mammogram. A sign, on this day of all days? No. There were other meanings, if you looked to such things for meanings. Death could come to anyone, at any age. To Mr. Dalton, much younger than she was. She was lucky. Lucky to be so well. Lucky to have survived. Mr. Dalton hadn't. Beth hadn't. Survivors — that word she despised, so freely used by those with little thought of what survival could mean. Concentration camp survivors, yes — they'd earned the name. Primo Levi survived — survived the death camps, wasn't able to survive his memories of them. She too was a survivor, she'd been told. Merely because she was still alive? We're all survivors, unless we're dead. If mere survival gets a medal, consider the cockroach, survivor extraordinary — and praise for that only if you were a cockroach. We take life so for granted. Waste it instead of treasuring it. Though there'd been a time in her own life when she hadn't set so high a value on it. Pray heaven no one had taken notes in that gloomy time, to use against her now.

"You sent for me. You've forgotten? Oh no, I'm not mistaken. Look: here's my memo. August 1982 it was . . . ."

"Do you go about pouncing on every rash utterance? That seems hardly fair."

"Ah, but it was no rash utterance. It was a deeply felt desire. Death would be welcome, you said. Why must you go on, you asked, day after day, alone, no longer needed by anyone? Your very words, my dear ...."

"But lots of people say something like that, at some time in their lives. They don't really mean it. I certainly didn't. I love my life." Now she did.

If things weren't right her doctor would call her. That poor girl, having to deal with such things. She'd just had her first child. Bad enough for a healthy young woman to have to examine this aging body: pray she wouldn't have to convey bad news. There'd be the phone call — the receptionist, asking her to come in, making an appointment. And she'd know there was something... Poor Linda! "First we'll do a biopsy. It may be nothing, but we have to be <u>sure</u>. Then after that ..." Or it could be worse; nothing to be done, the only question how long, how much more time she might have.

Linda would be sad, telling her. Nancy would tell her not to be. "Look, I'm an old woman. How long can it last? Don't be sad. I'll survive." (Though she wouldn't.)

Give it a week. If a week went by without a phone call, if Linda hadn't called by then, she could relax, shadows in those deep breasts notwithstanding. She'd be off the hook. And there was no real reason for her to worry. She'd never smoked, for one thing. That was in her favour. And no history of breast cancer in her family. They'd asked her about that. She made a conscious effort to tone down her optimism: never a good idea even at the best of times to challenge fate. Give it a week.

And she'd had this day. In the midst of winter's worst, coming on the day of her mammogram, she'd been given this bright, beautiful, glorious day. A gift. Though on this bright gift of a day Mr. Dalton had died. But he had a heart problem, he could have died at any moment. She must put that out of her thoughts; it had nothing to do with her really. She had this day, the joy of it to remember. Hold on to that.

Patience Wheatley

Patience Wheatley has written *A Hint of Spring, Goodbye to the Sugar Refinery, And Other Travels, More Garden Varieties,* and *Contemporary Poets*. She lives near Kingston, Ontario.

CANCER SEED

Driving
north into azalea spring,
then budding trees, the late winter
I called and called you
from every motel:
Jacksonville, Fayetteville,
Harrisburg, Kingston

I called again
from the Service Centre
near Brockville.

We'd planned a reunion
in Williamstown
after my working winter in Miami,
sisters-in-law together
for a gossip about the family.

But every time
the voiceless telephone
rang and rang
with never an answer

At last, at home in Montreal,
I hear from you:

Cataclysm!

a lumpectomy in Toronto
radiation and chemotherapy,
convalescence all summer.
Your mother had died of cancer,
your father must not be told.

We helped carry
your heavy secret,
your brother and I,
through years of anxiety
until your father died.

Then the secret's out.
Shocked friends gather to help
on and on until
warbling a siren tune
the threat shrivels
to a mere seed.

I WANT MORE

for a poet friend with cancer

Marcia told me to phone you at home
just across the park where you could watch
Jeremy on the swings as you worked at the window.

You sounded doubtful when I asked to join the group:
"They've been together months. Perhaps they're cruel ..."
"I'll come," I said. I remember so clearly

the red brick house, fallen on hard times, dark stairs with
hooks for coats that fell on the floor, the warm front room,
chairs ranged round the edges, a hanging plant, perhaps
carnivorous, books on radiators.

Our poems were full of death and blood.
We put down our friends' with instant cutting
judgement: "Can't relate to it." "Insults bus drivers!"

You listened to everyone. "I want more!" you said.

CALLING

How hard it is to talk about ...
How embarrassed we are by ...

Yet the threatened
want to talk.

We, the as yet healthy
must learn to talk warmly —
warmly with the stricken

The telephone lines are open
I can hear you.

I'll call and
call again.

Robert Chodos

Robert Chodos has been the editor of *Compass*, the magazine of the
Jesuits of English Canada, since 1987, and was principal of the
religious school at Temple Shalom, a Reform Jewish congregation
in Kitchener, Ontario, from 1986 to 1996. He is author or co-author of
ten books on Canadian political economy, most recently *Canada and
the Global Economy*. He lives in New Hamburg, Ontario.

KETURA: A MIDRASH

Abraham took another wife: her name was Ketura.
- Genesis 25:1

After Sarah died Abraham surveyed the wreckage of his life. One wife and son banished, wandering in the desert. The other wife dead, and their son an emotional cripple. Abraham was alone. He tried to sort out the voices that had haunted him all these years, the voice of Sarah and the voice of God.

— *Go forth from your land, your kindred, your father's house ...*

— *Abe, we have to leave! No one takes us seriously here. Here, you will always be the son of Terah the idol-maker.*

— *Where will we go?*

— *It doesn't matter. We could go anywhere — even to Canaan.*

— *Canaan! That's the end of the world! What would we do in Canaan?*

Sometimes he had been torn between the two voices, as when Sarah had urged him to try to talk God out of destroying Sodom and Gomorrah. He had never understood why Sarah had not talked to God herself. He never got anywhere with God, but sometimes God listened to Sarah. When God and Sarah agreed, Abraham didn't always like it, but at least he knew what he had to do.

— Cast them out! Get rid of that slave-woman and her son.

— God, she's being totally unreasonable. There's no arguing with her. All she says is "Get rid of them!"

— Do what she says!

— God, you don't mean that! Get rid of Hagar? And Ishmael, my firstborn son?

— Do what she says!

The memory of the morning when he had sent Hagar and Ishmael into the desert was still painful for Abraham. But there was an even more painful, and more recent, memory.

It had begun with the dream. In the dream Abraham had heard that unmistakable voice.

— Kill him! Offer up your son, the one you love, Isaac, as a sacrifice to me!

— God, you can't be serious. What about all those promises about my descendants numbering as the stars? All that was supposed to happen through Isaac, remember?

— I changed my mind. Offer up Isaac as a sacrifice.

— I have to talk to Sarah first. I can't do it without talking to Sarah.

— Sarah already knows.

Sarah had a dream that night too, and she woke up with a sense of deep foreboding. She looked out of the tent and saw Abraham leave at dawn with Isaac. She took a ram from their flock and followed a few paces behind, watching Abraham closely. He looked to her like a man possessed; she wondered if he was sleepwalking. All through the journey he never looked back, and he didn't know that Sarah was following. At the top of Mount Moriah she hid in the bushes with the ram as Abraham prepared the altar. When Abraham lifted the knife to slaughter Isaac she cried out:

— *Abraham! ABRAHAM!! Are you insane? How far do you have to go? If God told you to jump off a cliff, you'd do that too? ABRA ...*

The outcry awakened Abraham from his trance, although he did not place the voice as Sarah's. He looked up, saw the ram caught by its horns in the thicket, and sighed with relief. It must have been an angel calling to him, telling him that this was only a test. He sacrificed the ram while Isaac, shaking from the ordeal, looked on.

Then he noticed Sarah in the bushes, unconscious. Seeing Abraham's knife above Isaac's throat had been more than she could bear.

— *Isaac, help me take your mother back to Hebron.*

Isaac stared blankly.

Somehow, Abraham managed to get both of them home, but Sarah never regained consciousness, and she died a few days later. Isaac remained traumatised and uncommunicative, the shock of his father's betrayal compounded by his mother's death.

Sarah's voice was stilled and God's voice was silent, at least for now. But as he sorted through his memories, Abraham saw what had to be done, with unaccustomed clarity.

First, a burial plot. In all the years since they had come to Canaan, they had never needed one. Now Abraham bought a field from Ephron the Hittite and buried Sarah in the cave of Machpelah.

Then, arrangements had to be made for Isaac. He had begun to speak again, but it was obvious to Abraham that he would never recover completely. Even before Mount Moriah, Isaac had had a remote, otherworldly streak, and Sarah had cooked his food, washed his clothes, and made decisions for him. Who would take care of him now? It couldn't be Abraham; that wasn't his forte, and anyway, Isaac would never trust him. Isaac needed a wife, a woman of great inner strength and resourcefulness, and Abraham sent his trusted servant Eliezer to Mesopotamia to find this special person. Eliezer, bless him, came back with Rebecca. Rebecca who so reminded Abraham of Sarah. With Isaac in Rebecca's hands, the agitation and restlessness that had been Abraham's lot for years began to melt away. Now he could tend to his own needs.

* * *

She was a Canaanite, living near Hebron, a dark-eyed beauty who had often caught Abraham's eye. The loveliest woman in the area, but her beauty was not uncanny and disturbing like Sarah's. A delight to look at, that was all. Abraham was also drawn to her laugh, a laugh of uncomplicated joy, with none of the mocking, maniacal quality of Sarah's laugh.

When Abraham called on her father to ask for her in marriage, she was both frightened and thrilled. She knew about Hagar in the desert, and Sarah in the cave of Machpelah. If she became Abraham's wife, where would she end up? But Abraham was one of the wealthiest and most respected men in Canaan. He was old, that was true, but his vigour seemed undimmed. Her desires were conventional enough that the prospect of marriage with Abraham pleased her. She even accepted the Hebrew name he gave her: *Ketura*, my spicy one.

The years with Ketura were the happiest of Abraham's life. The days were spent tending their flocks and herds, entertaining guests who came to see the venerable patriarch, and caring for the sons Ketura bore in rapid succession — Zimran and Yokshan, Medan and Midyan, Yishbak and Shuah. No longer troubled by voices, not having anything to prove, not feeling any need to burden his new family with the God that had destroyed his first two marriages, he was at peace, now.

Ketura took pleasure in Abraham's happiness, and was happy herself, although in the early years she lived in constant fear that Abraham would again hear the voice of God. She was not interested in promises that her descendants would be numbered as the stars or would be a blessing to the nations. She knew the terrible price of such promises. But as time went on and God remained silent, she worried less. God was Isaac's problem now, or rather, Rebecca's.

Ketura did not even mind that Isaac would be Abraham's sole heir, that her own sons would not share in his inheritance, that as they grew up Abraham provided for them generously and sent them away so that the land could be Isaac's alone. In the tales that were already being spun about her husband, she was content to be a foot-note, a passing reference. Her happiness with Abraham was of the moment, but the moment was all that mattered to her. From what she saw, worrying about eternity brought only misery, and if Abraham disagreed with her about this, he never let it show.

Isaac and Rebecca visited only rarely, although they lived close by. In the years of Rebecca's barrenness, it pained her to see the ease with which Ketura bore children, and then later, after her twins were born, she had her hands full, especially since Isaac was not much help. When they did visit, the tension between Rebecca and Ketura was palpable. Rebecca considered Ketura an inferior and was jealous of her fertility. Mostly she held her tongue in Ketura's presence, but occasionally a disparaging remark about Canaanites would slip out. While Ketura quickly got used to those remarks, they made it diffi-cult for her to warm to Rebecca. Abraham, much as he loved Isaac and Rebecca, found himself wishing they would leave.

Somewhat more frequent, and more relaxed, were visits from Ishmael and his family, welcome in Abraham's tent again now that Sarah was no longer there. Ketura liked Ishmael's wife, a Canaanite like herself, better than anyone else in the family. She and Ketura talked while their children played happily together. Sometimes Ishmael's aged mother came, too. Hagar, who had been a slave but had nothing of the slave in her soul, won Ketura's respect if not her affection. Having known adversity all her life, and having overcome it, Hagar was every bit as tough and as capable as Rebecca, and yet unlike Rebecca, she never condescended to Ketura. Ketura sensed the spark between Hagar and Abraham that had still not been completely extinguished. She knew she would never have found her own place in Abraham's tent had it not been for the grim verdict pronounced on Hagar by Sarah and God.

Eventually Abraham began to fail. As he became weaker, Ketura sent for Isaac, Rebecca and the twins, for Ishmael and his family, and for her own sons whom Abraham had sent away. When Abraham died, Isaac and Ishmael, together for the first time since they were children, buried him beside Sarah in the cave of Machpelah. Rebecca, Jacob, Esau, old Hagar, Ishmael and his wife and children all crowded around the gravesite. Ketura, Zimran, Yokshan, Medan, Midyan, Yishbak and Shuah stood in the distance, watching. Their brief moment in Abraham's story was over. The vast and complex saga of his descendants would unfold without them.

Rienzi Crusz

Rienzi Crusz was born in Sri Lanka (Ceylon) and came to Canada in 1965. Educated at the universities of Ceylon, London (England), Toronto and Waterloo, his work has appeared in several Canadian and international journals and includes seven volumes of verse. *"Beatitudes of Ice"* is his latest book. He lives in Waterloo, Ontario.

CARPE DIEM

I pass
      yesterday's crooked milepost,
take in the night for erasure,
   fireflies, the timeless hour
of dreams.
   Closure is often
the death of pain, sweetness
   always lingers on.

And tomorrow   ?
   Will the monsoon rain
havoc among the tender paddies,
   expectations
slip like jello
            through my grasping fingers ?
Time   tomorrow,
   you are the mercury hour,
and I will not try
   to read your tarot soul or clasp
your ghostly hands.

So, today
      is the hugging moment,
when dawn walks in
      like a dear friend coming up the driveway;
today is the apple
      between my teeth, the song

fevered in my throat, the 'baila'
   that moves my old legs
to muscular dance.

And when the good earth
   sizzles in its high-noon fire,
I shall laze under this old Maple,
   read Neruda, and think
of Haputale's gentle rain, embracing mist,
   how poetry stalks the elephant,
fashions the raven into profound metaphor.

And then at evening,
   I'll still forget
the clocking hour, hunt memory
   for the small boy chasing the sand-crabs
with the blue ocean
   roaring in his ears,
for the honey in the fruit-bat's mouth,
   the dusk that takes in the raven
to autograph its Gauguin sky,

and remember
   the sun, the song, the dance,
the dance, the song, the sun.

"KNOW YOUR OWN BONE" (Thoreau)

Is my heart's passionate dance
    but a moth tempting the flame?
The long search   sweet discovery,
    you in dream,
the way you walked, walking
    with a Temple Flower in your hair,
choosing denial, the Belladonna way.

What do I see, or choose to see
    by morning light?
Why does the mind always make choices
    for the eye?
You, at the breakfast table,
    dispensing rituals
of CRISPIX cereal, orange juice, hot milk and toast;
    me, jousting with clock and laces,
winter boots that seem to shy
    from new journeys into the snow.

Night unravels the knotted muscle,
    makes room for dream, memory
that questions sad exits,
    chases the "whole bloody bird"
and ends up with a feather;
    must I remember the love I couldn't have,
forget the love of those I have?

Why, I ask my bones, is it harder to live
than to die?
Death in minute doses, small martyrdoms,
like afternoon's bland tuna sandwich,
the mailman's choice of junk mail and Christmas bills,
road-salt and arthritis on my snow-shovelling hands,
the body's slow disarmament!

And when I unearth these bones again,
gnaw at them slowly,
my father's riding the mathematical surf
like some Hawaiian beach boy,
as mother nurtures her restless brood of eight
with curried and embracing love,
rattan cane;
I see my wintered children
greening with summer,
my grandson, Jens, throbbing and thriving
on his Viking snows.

O Muse,
this bone that lets me suck
the sweet marrow of words,
is mine, stays here, is now —
no damp earth of burial,
no unearthing shovel's bruise;
but why those first mannerisms
of distrust?
how like a cruel sibling
you once held the candy under my nose,
then snatched it away and laughed.

Now that you've offered me the
heart of the flute,
be happy for the tapestries of my song,
The raven flies the world;
I hear the immigrant's voice, sweet and clear
as bamboo reed,

the elephant's trumpet
shatter the dark silences
of the snow lands.

DOWNSIZING

The Manager,
'HOUSE of FLOWERS'
Toronto   15. Jan. 1996
    Dear Madam,

                I am inquiring about your recent advertisement in the GLOBE & MAIL for a Dry Flowers Visual Assistant. Although my real expertise is in Reference and Book Collections Librarianship, specializing in Economics and Accounting Literature, I feel I have some talent in the business of flowers. Let me list some of my experience/s that may indicate my floral potentialities:

    I once helped my grandma Bess, who was an expert floral arranger, to prepare all the vases. My job was to fill one half of each vase with sand, the other half with crumpled old newsprint. I am frequently exposed to flowers, especially hybrid roses. My mother happens to be a rose garden nut, and depends on me to water her rose plants daily.

    Once, at the local flower shop, 'VALENTINE'S GARDEN', an expensive flower arrangement toppled from the counter to the floor. I immediately rearranged all the flowers in precisely the same order and height as they were originally in; I still remember how soft to the touch were the babies' breath. The lady at the counter could barely hide her amazement at my floral skills.

    Although I have short and stubby fingers, I feel, I know, I can manipulate flowers, dead or alive, in any way you want. How many times have the crocus, forsythia, sumac, and the red red rose appeared in my poems on spring and summer. This clearly demonstrates how much flowers lurk in my subconscious brain. And, not even a botanist can match the insights of a poet into the ways of flowers.

Believe me, madam, if you love something or somebody very much, you know how easy it is to manipulate that something or somebody. As I write, the cactus on my desk seems to be giving me a thorny look, maybe because I have not included it in my scheme of persuasion. It should have known by now that it's here only as a metaphor of survival, not as an argument for floral artistry.

I hope these notes will persuade you to treat this application favourably, and I look forward to hearing from you shortly.

Yours truly,
Lorna Buttermilk
BA (Hons), BLS (Toronto), MA

(Waterloo)

Anita Hanson

Anita Hanson's short stories and articles have appeared in several publications, including the *Toronto Star*, from which she received an honourable mention in its short story competition (1995). She lives in New Hamburg, Ontario.

PARADISE LOST

Linda entered Lunch a la Mode looking triumphant. "I've got it!" the petite brunette announced to the two women already seated at a corner table inside. "An idea that can't fail. Just can't."

Kathy and Margot looked dubious as Linda sat down, eyes shining. The three had been friends since high school, and 20 years later were still meeting regularly, cheering achievements, sharing confidences, and helping each other over life's hurdles. They were currently working on a hurdle faced by all three.

It had begun several months before when Margot, gentle brown eyes framed by wavy dark hair, had arrived for her birthday lunch looking decidedly glum. "I guess I shouldn't let it bother me," she said dispiritedly in response to their concerned questioning, "but sometimes I just wish for a little more ... um ... well ... romance, I guess, or affection, or ... something."

"Bob forgot your birthday, didn't he?" said Kathy, a sharp-featured blonde.

"No. He didn't forget. But he got me a T.V. for the bedroom."

"You hate watching T.V.," said Linda.

"Exactly," said Margot.

The subsequent conversation revealed a common thread of dissatisfaction. "The most romantic thing Mark has said to me in four years is, 'What's for supper?'" complained Kathy.

"At least he talks," said Linda.

Obviously, something had to be done. An active campaign had followed, hugely unsuccessful.

The candle-lit dinners in the dining room had been met with bewilderment (What? You mean just the two of us?). The roses sent to the office had been cause for great embarrassment ("Thank heavens the mushy card was in an envelope — I could pretend somebody had died."). The love notes tucked into the briefcases had gone unacknowledged, and the cellophane proved so unwieldy that it never made it to the door.

It was understandable then, that her friends had misgivings about Linda's new enthusiasm.

"It's like this," she went on, undeterred. "Chris, at work, has a big cottage up north that we can use the last weekend in September. Three bedrooms with separate bathrooms, right on the lake, with great hiking trails, a big fireplace. What could be more romantic? Walks in the fall leaves, canoe rides in the sunset, hot rum by the fire. Perfect!"

"Oh, it sounds wonderful," Margot said dreamily, "but I'm so afraid it still wouldn't work, and then what? Then there's just no hope at all." Kathy looked troubled, but Linda was more practical. "If this doesn't work, then we'll just have to try something else. I can't keep living like this."

This speech inspired an animated brainstorming session. The weekend would be a surprise — the men would be told to keep it free, but not what to expect. Child care would be arranged well in advance, meals planned carefully, to be prepared communally over glasses of chilled wine. Attractive lounge-wear would be required, and soft background music chosen. Even the most obdurate non-romantic could not help being won over. Excitement built as the idyllic getaway took shape.

* * *

The three cars arrived together early Friday evening after winding through tree-lined lanes down toward the water's edge. The women all jumped out immediately and exclaimed with delight over the picturesque cottage before them. Large and quite new, it still managed to effect a woody, rustic charm and fit unobtrusively into the landscape around it, blending perfectly into the trees and outcroppings of rock. A pebbly pathway led through September coloured bushes down to a small dock and boathouse on the water.

"Perfect, perfect, perfect!" cried Margot, all her doubts gone. She ran over to where Bob had joined the other men after all three had emerged somewhat more slowly from the vehicles. "Isn't it *perfect*?"

she repeated, grasping his arm.

He nodded absently, then turned his attention back to Greg, who was questioning Mark intently. "How did you manage to get here at the same time as us when we left before you?"

"Oh, I always take number 12 over to 26 to go north. People don't think of it because it's longer, but that means no traffic and clear sailing — a few more K's, but a lot less time." Greg tried not to look impressed, but was clearly going to remember this for the future.

At this point, Linda approached, clapping her hands. "O.K. everyone — let's get this stuff unloaded and get supper started. We're all hungry."

"We sure are," Greg grumbled. "Don't know why we couldn't have stopped for burgers on the way." The two others looked piqued as well, but the women ignored them.

The unloading was successfully accomplished, amid feminine oohs and aahs about the cottage's interior. A large, modern kitchen opened on to a warm, country-style dining room with a walk-out to a cedar deck overlooking the lake. Off the dining room, a snug living room beckoned with plump furniture, glowing wood walls and a huge fireplace flanked on both sides by overflowing bookshelves. Margot was ecstatic. "If this doesn't work, nothing will," she whispered to the others.

Supper plans were somewhat less successful. The men were taken aback to learn that they were expected to help with the preparations, and were not swayed by arguments that they would enjoy the togetherness and camaraderie. Kathy's suggestion that just this once they be excused to go cut firewood instead was not well received either. "What do we need a fire for?" Mark asked petulantly, as they were being shooed out the door. "This place has a furnace — I can hear it."

The mood was a bit sombre in the kitchen as knives clicked and sauces bubbled. "Not going too well, is it?" Margot said dejectedly. "Give it time," said Kathy, "Once they've had some food and a couple of drinks they'll be positively captivated."

The final dishes were just being put on the table when the men returned, arms full of firewood, chattering brightly. "Guess what we found?" Bob said excitedly. "There's a little outboard boat and all kinds of fishing equipment down in the boathouse. This weekend might not be so bad after all."

Supper was a quiet meal. The men threw nervous glances at each other, wondering what was wrong, while the women silently chewed their cioppino. The atmosphere improved slightly when in a moment of inspiration, Greg suggested that maybe the guys could do the dishes.

"Wonderful," said Linda. "You can start the fire, too, and that'll give us a chance to go up and change."

The fire was snapping cheerfully as the women came down the stairs in their new outfits, cozy leggings and fuzzy warm tops in a variety of pastel shades. "Victoria's Secret," whispered Margot to the others, blushing. "First time."

"Who'd like a hot rum?" Linda asked, walking into the freshly cleaned kitchen, where Bob had his head in the fridge. "Where's the beer?" he responded. "No beer," said Linda, "but there's wine left over from dinner." Three pairs of eyes widened in horror at this news. Mark recovered first, saying, "No problem — we can go into town and pick some up in the morning. I want to get to bed early tonight anyhow. I'm really bushed after that long drive."

Two heads nodded in agreement, and watches were consulted. "After ten already," said Greg, walking over to give Linda a quick buss. "I expect you girls will be up gossiping all night."

With that, they were gone, and the three women were left looking up the stairway after them. They fixed themselves drinks without speaking, then curled up in front of the fire, cradling the warm mugs in their hands. "Tomorrow will be different," said Linda grimly, "First we make it clear that there will be no fishing, then we'll have a relaxed day with a couple of quiet walks to get them into a mellow mood for the evening. This will work." They stared mutely into the dancing flames, each lost in her own thoughts until it was time for bed.

The following morning Linda and Margot were awakened by a very agitated Kathy. "Look what was on the table," she cried, waving a note in the air. They peered over her shoulders to read it together. "Gone into town for beer and bait. Hope we didn't wake you."

Linda sighed and tore up the note. "O.K. So we tell them when they get back."

They scrapped the plans for the herb omelette breakfast and decided to do some exploring. Down at the sun-warmed dock they first spent a few moments watching the glimmering water sparkle in the clear fall air, then turned unhappily to the boathouse where the little fishing boat hung suspended a few feet above the water. The walls were lined with rods, reels, and nets.

After a short walk they returned to the cottage but found the men had not yet arrived. The rest of the morning was spent disconsolately checking out the books by the fireplace, complaining, wandering in and out, and finally, preparing something to eat. Once again, the men arrived just as it was laid on the table.

"Sorry to be so long," Mark burbled, "but the guy at the bait shop was just great. Told us all the best places to go, and drew a map and everything. Even told us how to run the boat — turns out he knows Chris."

Lunch was a quiet meal, too. After being told that under no circumstances were they to go anywhere near the boathouse, the men slumped into their chairs and refused all suggestions for alternate activities. No walks. No board games. No trips to the gift shops in town. After eating, they each disappeared behind a section of the newspaper Bob had picked up that morning and all conversation ceased.

After cleaning up, the women wordlessly pulled on their jackets and went out for yet another walk on their own. Only the slam of the door communicated their intentions (and frame of mind) to their newspaper-absorbed husbands.

They returned an hour or so later to an empty house. "They wouldn't," said Kathy, then in a smaller voice, "Do you think they really would?" Linda approached the dining room table apprehensively and picked up another note lying there. "They did," she said quietly. Margot's eyes filled with tears, and the three of them moved soundlessly over to the big window and stared out at the shining lake.

* * *

It was about nine o'clock and long after dark when they finally decided to call the police. "They must have gone out about two," Kathy explained to the middle-aged officer, whose name was Dan, "and there's been no sign of them since." Linda was down showing Dan's young partner the boathouse, and Margot was too upset to talk at all.

"Did they know anyone around here? Anyone they might have gone to visit? Dan asked gently.

"No. No one," Kathy snuffled, breaking down.

They heard footsteps on the porch, and the other officer came in holding something in his hand. Linda followed, looking tired and pale.

"Did your husbands know anything about boats?" he asked.

"No," Kathy answered again. "They only ever fished from shore, and none of us ever spent much time around water. What is that thing?"

"It's the butt plug. It was sitting on a shelf in the boathouse," the young man said, and then reddened as Dan frowned and the three women looked at him blankly. "I mean ... um ... the boat's bilge draining plug. Boats all have a drain hole near the bottom, but of course the plug has to be in before it goes back in the water or it'll sink. Would they have known that?"

"I don't think so." The women all gathered around to look tearfully at the small object in the officer's hand — the small object that probably meant their husbands were at the bottom of the frigid lake.

* * *

By late Sunday afternoon there was still no word of the missing fishermen, and the police urged the three friends to pack up and go home where they would feel more comfortable. They stood sadly looking around the peaceful living room before locking up.

"It could have been so perfect," said Margot softly, "if only ..."

"Yes," said Linda, "if only." She then moved toward the books, readjusted the boat owner's manual on its shelf, and the three walked out, heads low.

Paul Knowles

Paul Knowles is a journalist, author and broadcaster. His books include *Home Run, A Matter of Conscience, Castle Kilbride: The Jewel of Wilmot Township*, and *The Fix*. With his wife, Mary, he is the editor and compiler of this book, *Close to the Heart*.
He lives in New Hamburg, Ontario.

OXFORD TRIPTYCH

FACE ONE: ODD VOLUMES

"So," he said, "you're the bookseller's dream customer. You've come to relieve me of all those old, broken-down books I have absolutely no use for."

If he had not been smiling, I would have probably turned on my heel and marched out of the store, muttering imprecations against those who malign their own customers. But he *was* smiling, his bearded face communicating a kind of comfortable warmth quite consistent with the volumes that filled every inch of shelving in his antiquarian book shop.

I had asked him the same question I had put to other book shop owners, all over Oxford, England. "Do you have any odd volumes? Say, pre-1800?"

I had thought it was a clever idea. I love old things, and I love books. Here, in the very heart of the written English word, I sought to combine my loves. However, having been subjected to the pointed stares of obviously wealthy owners in obviously expensive antiquarian book shops, I had lowered my sights a little. That's where the idea of odd volumes had its genesis.

An odd volume is an orphan from a larger set; volume three of the sermons of Bishop so-and-so, published in Cambridge in 1786, now permanently separated from its fellow volumes. The book has no real value to a serious — for serious, read ready-to-pay — book collector, but it is, none the less, ancient.

So I was cruising the lower-priced used book stores in Oxford, looking for a few nice odd volumes. Until: "You don't want odd volumes," said the book seller. "Not if you're really serious about enjoy-ing books."

I protested: "I love books."

"I believe you," he said. "You're just temporarily misguided."

He did have odd volumes in the shop. He even showed them to me, and he told me of the unending efforts of British booksellers to match them up with their former fellows. Book lovers carry Safeway bags of odd volumes to seminars and social gatherings, hoping to reassemble a set.

Does it happen?

"Rarely, if ever."

Other, more technologically oriented booksellers — some might feel there is something contradictory in the phrase — have started compiling lists, mailing mini-catalogs, and even, I suppose (although the "I" word was not breathed in that Oxford shop) posting the titles on the Internet. Actually, I think there would be something rather wonderfully ironic about reassembling a complete set of eighteenth century sermons by means of the World Wide Web. I digress.

We considered some of his odd volumes, each of us recognizing in the other the reverence and affection that is apparent in how one handles a book, opens it, page by careful page, and even in how one smells it. But in each and every case, he dissuaded me from pur-chase.

"You would be turning it into an ornament," he said. "It has no real use to you in its present form. And if you are the book person I think you are, you don't want to use a book as mere decoration."

If I wasn't his kind of book person before, I was now.

But, being North American and attuned to commerce on this side of the Atlantic, I awaited the sales pitch. "Now, if you really want something worthwhile, here, for only seventy-five pounds, I have ..." But it never came.

He inquired further about my interests. I explained that, as a Canadian, I was enthralled by the antiquity of so many things in Great Britain. Buildings, ruins, things Roman, and Saxon, and Norman — it leaves me breathless.

And thus, because I really do love books, I wanted to bring back one book printed before 1800, a book treasured and enjoyed by gener-ations of book lovers since it came into being. But I couldn't afford to pay two hundred pounds or more, the kind of price I'd been met with in the other shops.

He thought for a while, and admitted that he had nothing in his inventory that he could honestly recommend. But still, he wouldn't sell me one of his five pound, old, decrepit, odd volumes. He knew that in my heart, I truly wanted something better than that.

"What else are you interested in," he asked me?

I confessed my more modern affection for C.S. Lewis, and my passion to collect early and first editions of Lewis' books. He seemed interested. I told him such things were rare to unobtainable in Canada, but that since I had begun to visit England, I had found a few each trip.

We agreed that they were becoming more expensive with each passing year, especially since the biographical movie, *Shadowlands*, had been released.

He had no Lewis first editions; instead he asked what I had found on this trip. I told him of my most recent treasure — a first edition of *"Letters To Malcolm"*, bought at a book stand at a farmers' market in the southern town of Tavistock. For only two pounds fifty.

He rejoiced — there is no other word for it — in my find. He told me of a letter, hand-written and signed by C.S. Lewis, that he had purchased for two hundred pounds at an auction. He had intended it as an investment, but he now cannot bear to part with it.

I expressed envy; I felt kinship.

My wife found me in the shop, talking about Lewis with my new friend, whose name I never knew. But he made me promise that if I ever write a book about Lewis — a dream I shared easily with this stranger — I should come back to his shop and bring him a copy.

He sent me on my way, bidding us godspeed with as much enthusiasm as if he had sold me a first edition of Bunyan or a Milton folio. Instead, he had refused to sell me a thing.

And later that afternoon, I found in another shop a beautiful, pristine book entitled "Eight Charges Delivered to the Clergy of the Dioceses of Oxford and Canterbury to which are added Instructions to Candidates for Orders and a Latin Speech", by Thomas Secker L.L.D., published in 1770, bound in leather with gilt, and costing only thirty pounds. A glorious book, lovely to look at and fascinating to read.

I think my bookselling friend would have been as pleased as if he had sold it to me himself.

FACE TWO: V-E DAY IN STADHAMPTON

"Look, lads, it's Churchill, himself!"

Without question, he was the very image of Winston Churchill, swathed in a black overcoat, a dark fedora shadowing a face that often featured an equally dark scowl. He prowled around the grounds, entourage in tow, oblivious to the speculations concerning his costume and demeanor.

Which was probably just as well. Because while he was celebrating V-E day along with everyone else on the Stadhampton Common, it was unlikely that Churchill was first in his mind and memories. For the man in the black hat was entirely, proudly, enthusiastically, French.

He attended the English village's celebration of the 50th anniversary of V-E Day as an unofficial and unrecognized ambassador of his country in the same way as we were there as the only Canadians toasting with glasses of cider around the leaping fire. We knew his true identity through the happy accident that we were staying at the same bed and breakfast establishment — an ancient, sprawling manor house that looked out on the green where the celebrations were being held.

There were no speeches, or anthems, or marching bands, or even flags, in Stadhampton, a crossroads village just south of Oxford. As in innumerable small villages across the country, the V-E Day anniversary celebrations were more personal than pomp and circumstance. In other centres — before Buckingham Palace, or at Blenheim, for example — there was much ceremony. But the smaller villages found another way to celebrate.

For several days everyone for miles around had responded to the invitation to add any combustible materials to the growing pyramid in the common. There was wood, of course, from rough timbers to wooden furniture, and mattresses and cardboard boxes, and who knew what else. By the May evening when it was to be set aflame, the pile towered more than 25 feet high, and was at least that distance across. It would be quite the fire.

The bonfire was to be lit just after 8:30 p.m., at the same time as almost every village across England would set ablaze their own mound of lumber and cast-off combustibles. We emerged from the bed and breakfast, an unlikely, international crew that included our host and hostess, the dramatic Frenchman and his more retiring wife, their two English friends (sixty-five-ish sisters who ran a farm in Devon), and we two Canadians.

We joined a crowd that must have included every inhabitant of Stadhampton; the two village pubs would be empty tonight, at least until such time as the supply of beer and cider available at the tent — along with piping hot lamb stew — was exhausted.

Almost everyone knew almost everyone; this was not an occasion for political speeches or officious oratory. It was a village social, as people met, shared news, sipped a pint of cider, and, with few words or none, thought upon what is, and what might have been. About V-E Day, 50 years ago.

Just after 8:30, someone lit the bonfire. The flames leapt high. With our newfound acquaintances, we toasted ... in truth, it was a very imprecise, far-reaching toast, as we thought about the horror of war, and the bravery of warriors; of the freedom we take for granted; of the freedom that many others do not have, even now as the century wanes.

And we toasted the happy accidents that had brought a French couple, a Canadian couple, and two English sisters to a breakfast table in a 15th century manor house. There, over tea cups and toast racks, the conversation had ranged widely, in French and English — most often cracked and convoluted, but understood through patience and goodwill, or apparently understood through benevolent pretense. We had discussed the politics of France, and England, and Canada. We had learned how aging but fit sisters now raised horses in England, and how a then-younger, flamboyant French man once raised hell in New York City.

The evening before, seated around a manor house fireplace large enough to roast an ox (the very thing that had been done there on occasion, I'm sure), we had talked, and laughed, and celebrated our commonalities and our differences. It was there that we learned these four delightful eccentrics had long been friends, and had come to Oxford to celebrate V-E Day on the site where the English sisters had found themselves on that historic day, 50 years before.

So during the day, they had made their own trek, to Churchill's birthplace, and to the college at Oxford from whence had graduated this dynamic pair of farmers. This entire anniversary tour carried out, I do not doubt, with bilingual banter and pints of bitter.

But now, come evening, the bantering had passed. As the fire blazed high, and the glasses were held aloft, each of us toasted peace, and war, and the profound puzzle of humanity.

The folk of Stadhampton did not know who we were, or why we were there, eating their lamb stew and drinking their cider, on their village common. And at the very same time, we all knew, with clear inner vision, who we all were, and why we were there, and why we all, names unknown and nationalities unrevealed, matter very much to one another.

FACE THREE: TAVERN OF THE TRANSCENDENT

I looked for him in his church, at his college, and on those ancient paths along his river. But I found him in a pub.

It wasn't that he was absent, not exactly absent, in those other locales. He was there, all right, but only faintly; a ghost of the kind he would never have believed in, not ever. A faint echo; you might sense his presence, subtle and fleeting at best, but you could never touch him.

But when we sat down in the Lamb and Flag, on St. Giles Street in Oxford, England, and leaned earnestly over our pints of bitter, and spoke of things that mattered — Jack Lewis was there. Palpably, honestly, openly there.

There is no human being more important to the formation of who I am, what I believe, how I think, than is C.S. Lewis. In him I found someone who placed importance on the important things, and let the rest ride; a man of faith and friendship — no easy marriage in these schismatic days — who understood the simple pleasures of life, and could convey them through that magical, mystical, marvellous medium called "words". I rejoice always in the opening phrase of the Gospel of John — "In the beginning was the Word". In the beginning, and evermore, as well.

C.S. Lewis thought, and thought well, and after he had thought well and carefully and logically and thoroughly, he declared himself. First as a theist, and ultimately as a Christian. He took no credit for this, knowing that he was neither the pursuer nor the finder. He found no reason for pride in his embrace of the truth — rather, he found reason for humility, and awe, and — attend to this, all who believe to have once and for all fully grasped the truth of God — never-ending examination.

Much of my adult life has included C.S. Lewis. (I bear the abominable middle name Medford, and thus have at least a passing understanding of why "Clive Staples" became unchangeably "Jack" as soon as he could make the choice.)

Led by Lewis, I have explored Narnia, travelled to Malacandra, walked in the borderlands of heaven, and considered the correspondence of hell. I have pondered prayer along with Malcolm, reflected on the psalms, and observed grief. I have studied his work, those studies producing articles and an M.A. thesis.

All of which, in the normal course of things, should have found me led to consider Lewis as I would Shakespeare, or Eliot, or Erasmus; thematically, or theologically, or historically. Someone to be admired, read, and studied.

This is, in fact, what I expected when we planned our stay in Oxford.

I did not expect the wave of emotion, and the sense of presence that overtook me in the Lamb and Flag, a pub frequented by Lewis and his friends, the Inklings — J.R.R. Tolkein, Charles Williams, and the others.

Somehow, as Mary and I leaned into intimate conversation across a battered and worn, wooden tavern table, something incarnational occurred.

I know that echoes with sacrilege. But consider this: the miracle of Christ is that Word became Flesh. The divine became entirely human, spirit assumed substance.

In that Oxford pub, I experienced — sacrilege upon sacrilege? — transubstantiation in a tavern, the wonder of substantial spirit. We sat in a smoke-filled room, surrounded by undergraduates and other denizens of Oxford, with music playing and dozens of conversations filling the air. Once upon a time, the stories of Lewis, and Tolkein, and Williams were read aloud, word by word, line by line, in that very smoke-filled room, over pints of bitter and between puffs of pipe smoke.

And in that pub, we met Jack Lewis, more than 30 years after his death. There sat Lewis and his friends, intense in communication, their language seasoned with laughter. To my surprise, we experienced his joy, found in communion with friends, colleagues, and his God. All as real as life, and washed down with good, British beer.